Collins

# **AS** Revision**Notes**
# Chemistry

• Ann Tiernan •

Series editor: Jayne de Courcy

# CONTENTS

# HOW THIS BOOK WILL HELP YOU

We have planned this book to make your revision as easy and effective as possible.

Here's how:

## SHORT, ACCESSIBLE NOTES THAT YOU CAN INTEGRATE INTO YOUR REVISION FILE

*Collins Revision Notes AS Chemistry* has been prepared by a top examiner who knows exactly what you need to revise in order to be successful.

You can *either* base your revision on this book *or* you can tear out the notes and integrate them into your own revision file. This will ensure that you have the best possible notes to revise from.

## STUDENT-FRIENDLY PRESENTATION

The notes use lots of visual aids – diagrams, tables, flowcharts, etc. – so the content is easier to remember.

There is also systematic use of colour to help you revise:

| **MUST REMEMBER** | **MUST TAKE CARE** | **MUST KNOW** |
|---|---|---|
| Red panels highlight essential content. | Purple panels highlight areas where students often make mistakes. | Green panels highlight some important points. |

– Red type identifies key terms.
– Green type identifies key definitions.
– Yellow highlight is used to emphasise important words and phrases.

## CONTENT MATCHED TO YOUR SPECIFICATION

The Contents/Specification Matching Grid on pages ii–iii lists each short topic and shows which specifications it is relevant to. This means you know exactly which topics you need to revise.

In some topics, there are short sections that are only relevant to one or two specifications. These are clearly marked.

## GUIDANCE ON EXAM TECHNIQUE

This book concentrates on providing you with the best possible revision notes.

Worked Examples are also included in each topic to help you with answering exam questions. If you want more help with exam technique, then use the exam practice book alongside these Revision Notes: *Collins Exam Practice AS Chemistry*.

Using both these books will help you to achieve a high grade in your AS Chemistry exams.

# ATOMIC STRUCTURE

## ELEMENT SYMBOLS

The element symbol gives information about the structure of an atom of the element.

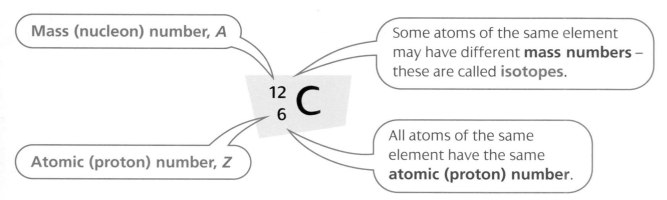

Mass (nucleon) number, A

Some atoms of the same element may have different **mass numbers** – these are called **isotopes**.

$$^{12}_{6}\text{C}$$

All atoms of the same element have the same **atomic (proton) number**.

Atomic (proton) number, Z

- An atom contains:
  - **protons** and **neutrons** in the **nucleus**
  - **electrons** arranged in shells and subshells.

This is the same as the number of electrons in an uncharged atom.

**The atomic (proton) number is defined as the number of protons in the nucleus.**

**The mass (nucleon) number is defined as the total number of protons and neutrons.**

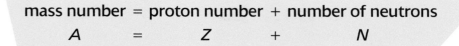

$$\text{mass number} = \text{proton number} + \text{number of neutrons}$$
$$A = Z + N$$

The **mass (nucleon) number** is the total number of **protons** and **neutrons** in the nucleus.

$$^{12}_{6}\text{C}$$

The **atomic (proton) number** is the number of **protons** in the nucleus.

In a neutral atom the number of **protons** and **electrons** are **equal**.

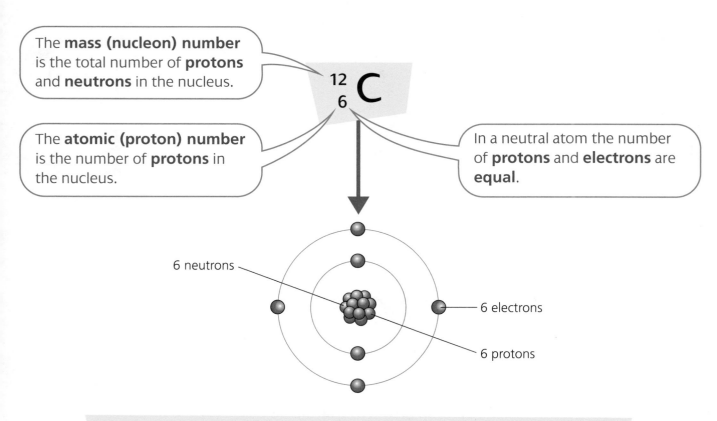

6 neutrons

6 electrons

6 protons

**Carbon**: Atomic (proton) number 6:    6 protons and 6 electrons
Mass (nucleon) number 12:    total 12 = 6 protons + 6 neutrons

# MASS AND CHARGE

**MUST REMEMBER**

- **Protons** and **neutrons** have **relative mass of 1**.
- The protons and neutrons in the nucleus give the atom its mass.
- **Electrons** have a **negligible** (very small) mass.

**MUST REMEMBER**

- **Protons** have a charge of **+1**.
- The protons give the nucleus its positive charge.
- **Neutrons** have **no charge**.
- **Electrons** have a charge of **−1**.

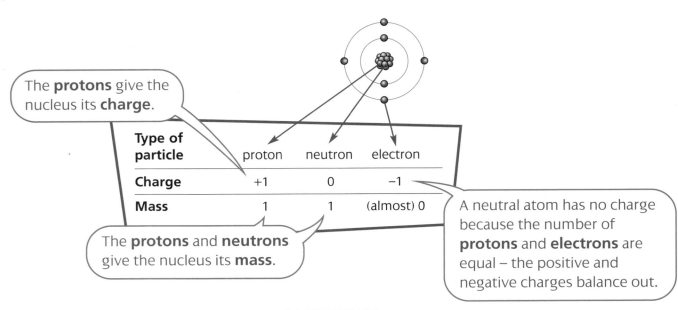

The **protons** give the nucleus its **charge**.

| Type of particle | proton | neutron | electron |
|---|---|---|---|
| Charge | +1 | 0 | −1 |
| Mass | 1 | 1 | (almost) 0 |

The **protons** and **neutrons** give the nucleus its **mass**.

A neutral atom has no charge because the number of **protons** and **electrons** are equal – the positive and negative charges balance out.

## ISOTOPES

**MUST REMEMBER**

- **Isotopes** are atoms of the **same element** that have different masses.
- They have the **same atomic number** but **different mass numbers**.
- They have the **same number of protons** but **different numbers of neutrons**.

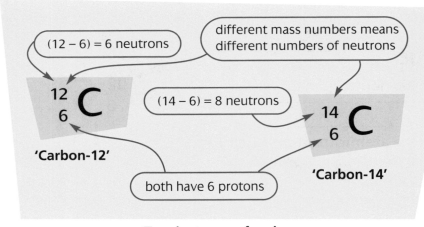

$(12 - 6) = 6$ neutrons

different mass numbers means different numbers of neutrons

$^{12}_{6}C$

'Carbon-12'

$(14 - 6) = 8$ neutrons

$^{14}_{6}C$

'Carbon-14'

both have 6 protons

**Two isotopes of carbon**

**WORKED EXAMPLE**

The atomic number, Z, and mass number, A, of two types of atom are shown in the table. Identify the atoms and give the number of protons and neutrons in the nucleus of each.

| | Z | A |
|---|---|---|
| **Atom 1** | 35 | 81 |
| **Atom 2** | 35 | 79 |

Both have atomic (proton) number 35, so they are both **bromine**.
They are **isotopes** because they have different mass numbers.
(Atom 1) Bromine-81 contains **35 protons** and **46 neutrons** (81 − 35).
(Atom 2) Bromine-79 contains **35 protons** and **44 neutrons** (79 − 35).

# THE MASS SPECTROMETER AND RELATIVE ATOMIC MASS

## THE MASS SPECTROMETER

The mass spectrometer measures the mass of particles, including atoms.

### HOW IT WORKS

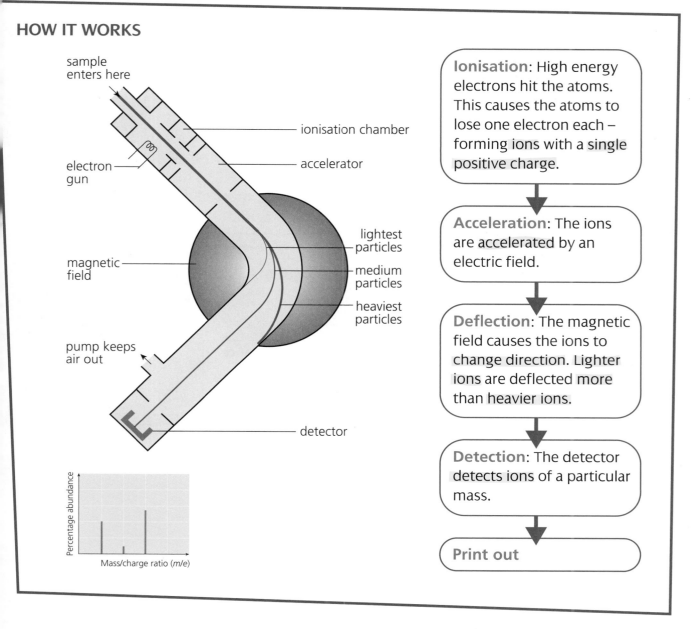

Ionisation: High energy electrons hit the atoms. This causes the atoms to lose one electron each – forming ions with a single positive charge.

Acceleration: The ions are accelerated by an electric field.

Deflection: The magnetic field causes the ions to change direction. Lighter ions are deflected more than heavier ions.

Detection: The detector detects ions of a particular mass.

Print out

## MASS SPECTRA DATA

Data can be presented in a table or a graph:

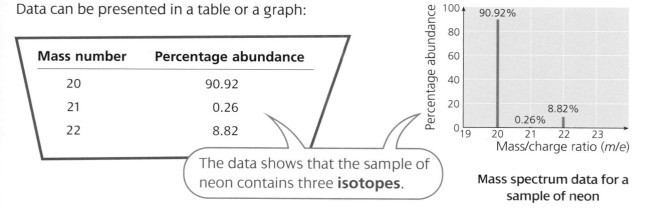

| Mass number | Percentage abundance |
|-------------|----------------------|
| 20          | 90.92                |
| 21          | 0.26                 |
| 22          | 8.82                 |

The data shows that the sample of neon contains three **isotopes**.

Mass spectrum data for a sample of neon

# RELATIVE ATOMIC MASS

## THE RELATIVE MASS SCALE

- Masses of atoms are measured using the relative mass scale:
  - Carbon-12 is the standard and its mass is given the value of exactly 12.
  - Masses of other atoms are given values by using this scale and so their masses are relative to carbon-12.

$$^{12}_{\ 6}\text{C}$$

### MUST REMEMBER

- The isotopic mass of an isotope is the relative mass of one atom of that isotope compared to $\frac{1}{12}$ the mass of one atom of carbon-12.
- The relative atomic mass ($A_r$) of an element is the average relative mass of its atoms – taking into account its isotopes and their abundances – compared to one atom of C-12.

- The Periodic Table shows the relative atomic mass of elements to several decimal places.

- Naturally occurring carbon contains small amounts of $^{14}\text{C}$ so the average mass of its atoms is 12.01 not 12.

12.01
C
6

## CALCULATING THE RELATIVE ATOMIC MASS OF CHLORINE

The naturally occurring isotopes of chlorine are shown in the table. Calculate the relative atomic mass of chlorine.

| Mass number | Percentage abundance |
| --- | --- |
| 35 | 75 |
| 37 | 25 |

Step 1: work out the relative mass of 100 atoms of chlorine

In 100 atoms, 75 have a mass of 35, total mass: $75 \times 35 = 2625$

In 100 atoms, 25 have a mass of 37, total mass: $25 \times 37 = 925$

Add these together

Total mass of 100 atoms: $= 3550$

Step 2: work out the average mass of 1 atom

Relative atomic mass: $\dfrac{3550}{100} = 35.5$

Divide by 100

35.5
Cl
17

There are more atoms of chlorine-35 than chlorine-37 so the average mass of a chlorine atom is 35.5 not 36.

### WORKED EXAMPLE

Calculate the relative atomic mass of magnesium from the following data.

| Isotope | Percentage abundance |
| --- | --- |
| $^{24}\text{Mg}$ | 78.6 |
| $^{25}\text{Mg}$ | 10.1 |
| $^{26}\text{Mg}$ | 11.3 |

Relative atomic mass $= \dfrac{(78.6 \times 24) + (10.1 \times 25) + (11.3 \times 26)}{100} = 24.3$

# IONISATION ENERGIES

## WHAT 'FIRST IONISATION ENERGY' MEANS

Ionisation energy gives an idea of how much energy is needed to take electrons away from atoms so that they form **positive ions**.

### FIRST IONISATION ENERGY

**The first ionisation energy is defined as the energy needed to remove one mole of electrons from one mole of gaseous atoms to form one mole of ions with a single positive charge.**

Energy values are measured **per mole**.

General equation $\quad X(g) \rightarrow X^+(g) + e^-$

e.g. $\quad Mg(g) \rightarrow Mg^+(g) + e^- \qquad \Delta H = +738\,kJ\,mol^{-1}$

Atoms are **gases** when the measurements are made.

**One electron** is removed from each atom, so the ion has a **single positive charge**.

$\Delta H$ **is positive**, showing this is an **endothermic change – energy is taken in**.

## FIRST IONISATION ENERGIES AND ELECTRON SHELLS

- First ionisation energies give evidence for the idea that electrons are arranged in shells.

- Electrons are held by the positive charge on the nucleus so electrons in shells closer to the nucleus are held more strongly than those in shells further away.

### FIRST IONISATION ENERGIES FOR GROUP 2

| Element | Electron configuration | First ionisation energy / kJ mol⁻¹ |
|---------|------------------------|-------------------------------------|
| Be | 2,2 | 900 |
| Mg | 2,8,2 | 738 |
| Ca | 2,8,8,2 | 590 |

- It takes **less energy** to remove an electron from atoms **further down a group** because:
  - The outer electron shell is **further away from the nucleus**.
  - There is more shielding because there are **more inner electrons shells**.
  - The increase in positive charge on the nucleus has **less effect** than the **increased shielding**.

# REMOVING MORE ELECTRONS

The energy needed to remove more – successive – electrons from the same atom gives more evidence that electrons are arranged in shells in the atom. For example, magnesium has an **electron configuration** of 2,8,2.

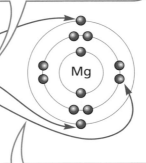

The first two electrons removed are from the third shell ($n = 3$).

## IONISATION ENERGIES OF MAGNESIUM

| First ionisation energy | $Mg(g) \rightarrow Mg^+(g) + e^-$ | $\Delta H = +738 \, kJ \, mol^{-1}$ |
|---|---|---|
| Second ionisation energy | $Mg^+(g) \rightarrow Mg^{2+}(g) + e^-$ | $\Delta H = +1451 \, kJ \, mol^{-1}$ |
| Third ionisation energy | $Mg^{2+}(g) \rightarrow Mg^{3+}(g) + e^-$ | $\Delta H = +7733 \, kJ \, mol^{-1}$ |

### MUST REMEMBER

- Each **successive ionisation energy** is **bigger than the last** because there are fewer electrons (less negative charge) but the positive charge on the nucleus is the same, so the 'pull' on each electron is **greater**.

- Electrons from shells **closer to the nucleus** need **much more energy** to be removed because they are **less shielded by inner electrons** from the charge on the nucleus.

It takes **much more energy** (5 times as much here!) to remove the third electron because it is in the second shell ($n = 2$).

# SUCCESSIVE IONISATION ENERGY GRAPHS

**Successive ionisation energy graphs** show the energy needed to take all the electrons from a single type of atom.

## SUCCESSIVE IONISATION ENERGIES OF MAGNESIUM

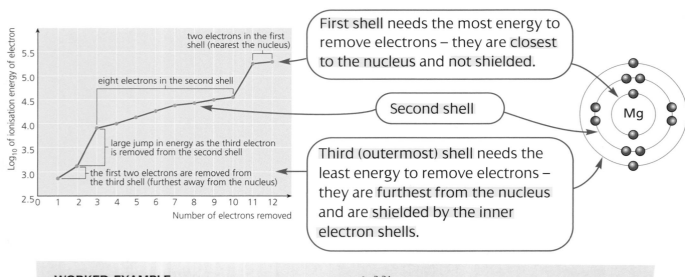

First shell needs the most energy to remove electrons – they are closest to the nucleus and not shielded.

Second shell

Third (outermost) shell needs the least energy to remove electrons – they are furthest from the nucleus and are shielded by the inner electron shells.

### WORKED EXAMPLE

Look at this graph of successive ionisation energies for an atom.
(a) Identify the atom.
(b) Explain why the first and second ionisation energies are so different.

(a) The atom has 11 electrons. From the graph, the configuration is 1,8,2. The atom is sodium.
(b) The first ionisation energy is for an electron being removed from the third shell. The second ionisation is much higher because the electron is removed from second shell. The second shell electrons are closer to the nucleus and are less well shielded.

# ELECTRON CONFIGURATIONS

## ELECTRON SHELLS AND SUBSHELLS

- **Electron shells** have **quantum numbers**. The first shell is n = 1.
- Each shell has smaller **subshells**, for example 1s, 2s and 2p.
- Each subshell has a different **energy level**.
- s subshells have lower energy levels than p subshells.
- The electrons in an atom fill the lowest energy level that is available.

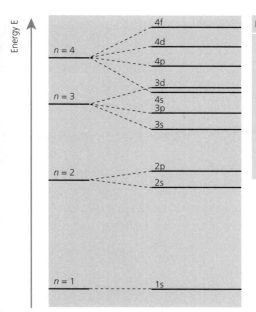

| Principal quantum number, n | Shell number | Subshells | Maximum number of electrons | |
|---|---|---|---|---|
| 1 | 1 | 1s | 2 | Total = 2 |
| 2 | 2 | 2s | 2 | Total = 8 |
| | | 2p | 6 | |
| 3 | 3 | 3s | 2 | Total = 18 |
| | | 3p | 6 | |
| | | 3d | 10 | |
| 4 | 4 | 4s | 2 | Total = 32 |
| | | 4p | 6 | |
| | | 4d | 10 | |
| | | 4f | 14 | |

### MUST KNOW

- The **number of electrons** in each subshell up to 4s.
- The **order of subshells** up to 4s (remember: 3d is higher than 4s!!).

## IONISATION ENERGIES AND SUBSHELLS

Looking at the pattern of first ionisation energies across a period gives evidence that electron shells contain subshells at different energy levels.

**First ionisation energies against atomic number**

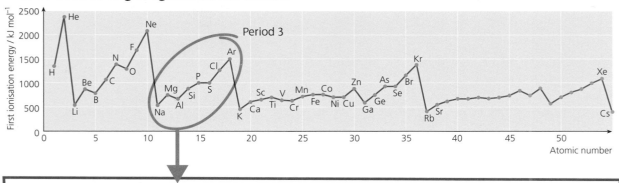

### KEY POINTS ABOUT IONISATION ENERGIES ACROSS PERIOD 3

- The first electron removed from every atom is from the third shell (n = 3).
- The electrons are all shielded by two inner shells.
- The general trend is an increase, as the nuclear charge increases.
- The first ionisation energies of aluminium and sulphur 'dip'.
- The third shell contains a 3s subshell and a 3p subshell at different energy levels.
- The 2,3,3 pattern is caused by electrons being removed from the single s or the three p orbitals.
- The other periods also show 'dips and peaks' due to subshells.

# WORKING OUT ELECTRON CONFIGURATIONS OF ATOMS AND IONS

## EXAMPLES

| Element | Proton number | Electronic configuration of atom | Electronic configuration of ion |
|---|---|---|---|
| calcium | 20 | Ca: $1s^2 2s^2 2p^6 3s^2 3p^6 \textbf{(3d}^0\textbf{)4s}^2$ | $Ca^{2+}$: $1s^2 2s^2 2p^6 3s^2 3p^6 \textbf{(3d}^0\textbf{)4s}^0$ |
| titanium | 22 | Ti: $1s^2 2s^2 2p^6 3s^2 3p^6 \textbf{3d}^2\textbf{4s}^2$ | $Ti^{2+}$: $1s^2 2s^2 2p^6 3s^2 3p^6 \textbf{3d}^2\textbf{4s}^0$ |

**4s electrons are lost first** when atoms form ions.

## s AND p ORBITALS

- Electrons in a subshell occupy **orbitals**.
- An orbital represents the space in which fast-moving electrons are most likely to be found.
- Each orbital carries **two electrons**.
- s subshells have a **single s orbital**.
- p shells contain **three p orbitals** (see the 2,3,3 pattern in the first ionisation across Period 3).

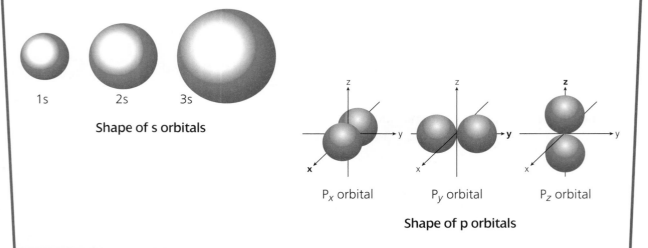

1s    2s    3s

Shape of s orbitals

P$_x$ orbital    P$_y$ orbital    P$_z$ orbital

Shape of p orbitals

---

**WORKED EXAMPLE**

(a) Describe the arrangement of protons, neutrons and electrons in an atom of zinc (proton number 30, mass number 65).

(b) How does this arrangement differ from the arrangement in a zinc ion, $Zn^{2+}$?

(a) **Zinc atom**:
Proton number 30: There are **30 protons** and **30 electrons**.
Mass number 65: There are $(65 - 30) = $ **35 neutrons**.
The protons and neutrons are in the nucleus. The electrons are arranged in shells and subshells.
The electronic configuration is: $1s^2 2s^2 2p^6 3s^2 3p^6 3d^{10} 4s^2$

(b) **Zinc ion, $Zn^{2+}$**:
The arrangement of protons and neutrons is the same. Two electrons are lost from the 4s subshell.
The electronic configuration is: $1s^2 2s^2 2p^6 3s^2 3p^6 3d^{10} 4s^0$

# THE MOLE

## WHAT IS A MOLE?

> The mole measures the **amount** of particles in a substance.

**Definition: one mole is the amount of substance that contains as many particles as there are atoms in exactly 12 g of carbon-12.**

> The actual number of particles in one mole is $6 \times 10^{23}$. This is called **Avogadro's constant**.

> Carbon-12 is used as the 'standard' – exactly the same standard is used for measuring relative mass.

## THE MOLE AND RELATIVE ATOMIC MASS

- Different types of atoms have different relative atomic masses.
- Therefore the same amount of different types of atoms have different masses.

**The relative atomic mass in grams of any element contains one mole of atoms.**

12 g carbon-12

24 g magnesium

$A_r$ of carbon-12 = 12. 12 g of carbon-12 contain one mole of atoms.

$A_r$ of magnesium = 24. Magnesium atoms are twice as heavy as carbon atoms. 24 g of magnesium contain one mole of atoms.

> Both samples contain the **same amount of atoms** = **one mole** ($6 \times 10^{23}$ atoms).

# THE MOLE AND RELATIVE MOLECULAR MASS $M_r$

> **Definition: the relative molecular mass of a compound is the mass of its formula unit – relative to $\frac{1}{12}$ the mass of an atom of carbon-12.**

> The **formula unit** is the **formula** of the substance (see below).

> The same carbon-12 scale is used.

- The **formula unit** is the formula – this can show the number of atoms in a molecule or the simplest ratio of atoms in a giant structure.

## EXAMPLES

### Carbon dioxide $CO_2$

$A_r$ C = 12, $A_r$ O = 16
$M_r$ = 12 + (2 × 16) = 44
Molar mass = 44 g mol$^{-1}$

- 1 mole of carbon dioxide contains 1 mole of carbon dioxide molecules.
- 1 mole of carbon dioxide molecules contains 1 mole of carbon atoms and 2 moles of oxygen atoms.

### Magnesium oxide MgO

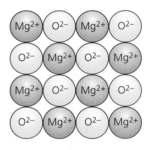

$A_r$ Mg = 24, $A_r$ O = 16
$M_r$ = 24 + 16 = 40
Molar mass = 40 g mol$^{-1}$

- 1 mole of magnesium oxide contains 1 mole of magnesium oxide formula units, MgO – this is the simplest ratio of atoms – magnesium oxide does not exist as separate molecules.
- 1 mole of magnesium oxide contains 1 mole of magnesium ions and 1 mole of oxide ions.

## MOLE CALCULATIONS

### MUST REMEMBER

- Number of moles = $\dfrac{\text{mass in grams}}{\text{molar mass}}$

### MUST KNOW

- How to work out the number of moles from the mass.
- How to work out the mass from the number of moles.

### WORKED EXAMPLES

(a) **How many moles of sulphur dioxide are contained in 32 g?**

Molar mass of $SO_2$ = 32 + (2 × 16) = 64

Number of moles = $\dfrac{\text{mass in grams}}{\text{molar mass}} = \dfrac{32}{64} = 0.5$ moles

(b) **What is the mass of 1.5 moles of magnesium carbonate?**

Mass of 1 mole of $MgCO_3$ = 24 + 12 + (3 × 16) = 84 g
Mass of 1.5 moles = 1.5 × 84 = 126 g

# EMPIRICAL AND MOLECULAR FORMULAE

## EMPIRICAL FORMULAE

**MUST KNOW**

• The **empirical formula** is the **simplest whole-number ratio** of the number of atoms of each element in a compound.

• Empirical formulae can be calculated from data about **percentage masses**.

• For organic compounds, this data often comes from combustion analysis – burning a compound and measuring the amount of carbon dioxide and water that are formed.

### HOW TO CARRY OUT CALCULATIONS

A compound contains 52.2% carbon, 13.0% hydrogen and 34.8% oxygen. What is its empirical formula?

**Step 1:** work out the **masses in grams** of each element in **100 g of the compound**

**Step 2:** work out the **number of moles** of each element:
$$\text{No. of moles} = \frac{\text{mass in grams}}{\text{molar mass}}$$

**Step 3:** work out the **simplest ratio** by dividing by the smallest number – this ratio must have **whole numbers**

**Step 4:** write the **formula**

| | carbon | hydrogen | oxygen |
|---|---|---|---|
| 100 g contains | 52.2 g | 13.0 g | 34.8 g |
| Number of moles | $\frac{52.2}{12} = 4.35$ | $\frac{13.0}{1} = 13.0$ | $\frac{34.8}{16} = 2.175$ |
| Simplest ratio | $\frac{4.35}{2.175} = 2$ | $\frac{13.0}{2.175} = 5.97$ | $\frac{2.175}{2.175} = 1$ |
| | 2 | 6 | 1 |
| Formula | | $C_2H_6O$ | |

**WORKED EXAMPLES**

(a) What is the empirical formula of ethane, $C_2H_6$?
The empirical formula is the **simplest ratio** of atoms.
Empirical formula of ethane is $CH_3$.

(b) A hydrocarbon contains 75% carbon. What is its empirical formula?

In 100 g there are 75 g carbon therefore 25 g hydrogen
Number of moles = 75/12 = 6.25 carbon 25/1 = 25 hydrogen
Simplest ratio 6.25/6.25 = 1 25/6.25 = 4
Empirical formula is $CH_4$.

# MOLECULAR FORMULAE

**Molecular formulae:**

- show the actual number of atoms present in a molecule
- are worked out using relative molecular mass data from the mass spectrometer.

## HOW TO WORK OUT MOLECULAR FORMULAE

The empirical formula of a compound is CH. Its relative molecular mass is 78. What is the molecular formula?

**Step 1: work out the relative mass of the empirical formulae**

→ Relative mass of CH = 12 + 1 = 13.

Mass of one molecule = 78

→ Number of empirical formula units = $\frac{78}{13}$ = 6

**Step 2: work out how many empirical formula units there are in one molecule**

Therefore, multiply empirical formula by 6 to give molecular formula = **$C_6H_6$**.

## WORKING WITH EMPIRICAL AND MOLECULAR FORMULAE

**Ethane**

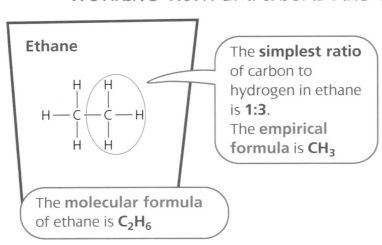

The **simplest ratio** of carbon to hydrogen in ethane is **1:3**.
The **empirical formula** is **$CH_3$**

The **molecular formula** of ethane is **$C_2H_6$**

**Ethanoic acid**

Molecular formula: $C_2H_4O_2$
(usual formula $CH_3COOH$)
Empirical formula: $CH_2O$

## OTHER EXAMPLES

|  | Molecular formula | Empirical formula |
|---|---|---|
| Ethane | $C_2H_6$ | $CH_3$ |
| Propene | $C_3H_6$ | $CH_2$ |
| Methane | $CH_4$ | $CH_4$ |

### WORKED EXAMPLE

A compound contains 5.9% hydrogen and 94.1% oxygen. It has a molar mass of 34 g. What is its molecular formula?

| 100 g contains | 5.9 g hydrogen | 94.1 g oxygen |
|---|---|---|
| Number of moles = | 5.9/1 = 5.9 | 94.1/16 = 5.9 |
| Simplest ratio | 1 : | 1 |
| **Empirical formula** | HO | |

Work out the **empirical formula** first.

Molar mass = 34 g. Mass of empirical formula = 17 g
**Molecular formula** is $H_2O_2$ (hydrogen peroxide).

# EQUATIONS AND MASS CALCULATIONS

## HOW TO WRITE EQUATIONS

Step 1: write a **word equation**

Step 2: write down the **correct formulae**

Step 3: **balance** the equation

Step 4: add **state symbols** if needed

magnesium + hydrochloric acid → magnesium chloride + hydrogen

$Mg(s)$ + $2HCl(aq)$ → $MgCl_2(aq)$ + $H_2(g)$

**Example**

Write an equation, with state symbols, to show the complete combustion of methane to produce carbon dioxide and water.

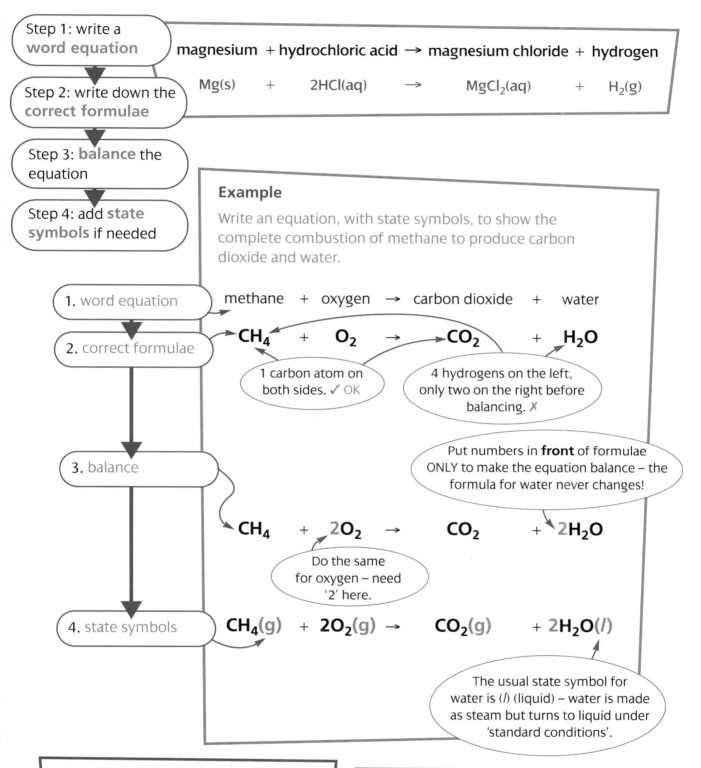

1. word equation

methane + oxygen → carbon dioxide + water

2. correct formulae

$CH_4$ + $O_2$ → $CO_2$ + $H_2O$

1 carbon atom on both sides. ✓ OK

4 hydrogens on the left, only two on the right before balancing. ✗

Put numbers in **front** of formulae ONLY to make the equation balance – the formula for water never changes!

3. balance

$CH_4$ + $2O_2$ → $CO_2$ + $2H_2O$

Do the same for oxygen – need '2' here.

4. state symbols

$CH_4(g)$ + $2O_2(g)$ → $CO_2(g)$ + $2H_2O(l)$

The usual state symbol for water is (*l*) (liquid) – water is made as steam but turns to liquid under 'standard conditions'.

## STATE SYMBOLS

(g)  gas

(*l*)  liquid – this symbol is used for water in most reactions

(s)  solid or a precipitate

(aq)  aqueous solution – used for a substance dissolved in water

## OTHER SYMBOLS

→  is the usual symbol used in equations

⇌  is used when the reaction is **reversible** and so reaches **equilibrium**

# MASS CALCULATIONS FROM EQUATIONS

A **balanced equation**:

- gives the **amount in moles** of each substance involved
- can be used to work out the **masses of substances** in the reaction.

Four steps for working out reacting masses:

> Step 1: write a **balanced equation**

> Step 2: write the **amounts (in moles)** of the substances in the question

> Step 3: change moles into **masses**

> Step 4: **scale** the masses to the question

**|| MUST TAKE CARE ||**

Some exam questions may use tonnes instead of grams – the method is the same!

## Example

What mass of carbon dioxide is made when 64 g of methane are burned?

*Look at the question – only methane and carbon dioxide are mentioned.*

1. balanced equation → $CH_4 \; + \; 2O_2 \; \rightarrow \; CO_2 \; + \; 2H_2O$

2. amounts (in moles) → 1 mole     1 mole

3. masses → $[12 + 4 =]$ 16 g     $[12 + (2 \times 16) =]$ 44 g

*Work out how much carbon dioxide 1 g of methane makes by dividing through by 16.*

4. scale to question → 1 g     $\dfrac{44 \text{ g}}{16}$

      64 g     $\dfrac{44 \times 64 = 176 \text{ g}}{16}$

*Sometimes the 'scale up' is easy to spot – here, 64 is four times 16, so the right answer could come from multiplying through by 4! $(4 \times 44 = 176 \text{ g})$.*

176 g of carbon dioxide are made.

## WORKED EXAMPLE

Coal burnt in power stations contains sulphur.
The sulphur burns with the coal and makes the pollutant gas sulphur dioxide.
How many tonnes of sulphur dioxide are produced when 16 tonnes of sulphur burns?

(equation)   $S + O_2 \rightarrow SO_2$
(moles)      1 mole S makes 1 mole $SO_2$
(masses)    32 g S makes 64 g $SO_2$
(scale)      32 tonnes S makes 64 tonnes sulphur dioxide
             16 tonnes S makes 32 tonnes of sulphur dioxide

**|| MUST TAKE CARE ||**

In exams, marks get scored for **working** as well as for the **final answer**. Setting the method out clearly will gain marks, **even if the final answer is wrong**.

*The question is in tonnes – convert both masses to tonnes and then the pattern is clear: divide both by 2.*

# PERCENTAGE YIELDS

## WHAT IS ACTUAL YIELD?

Some experiments involve making a chemical product. The success of the experiment can be measured by comparing **theoretical yield** with **actual yield**.

**Theoretical yield is:**

- **the maximum amount of product that can be made from the available reactants**
- **calculated from the amounts of the reactants using the balanced equation.**

**Actual yield is:**

- **the amount of product that is actually made, measured at the end of the reaction.**

## WHY IS ACTUAL YIELD ALWAYS LESS THAN THEORETICAL YIELD?

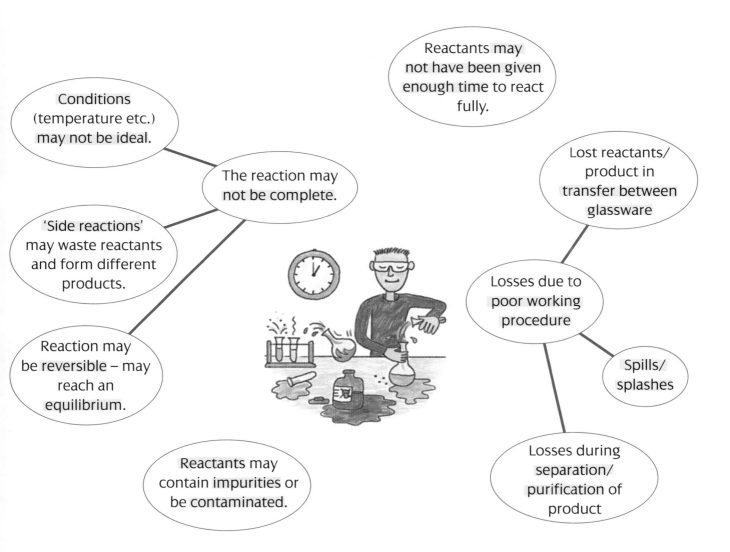

Reactants may not have been given enough time to react fully.

Conditions (temperature etc.) may not be ideal.

The reaction may not be complete.

Lost reactants/ product in transfer between glassware

'Side reactions' may waste reactants and form different products.

Losses due to poor working procedure

Reaction may be reversible – may reach an equilibrium.

Spills/ splashes

Reactants may contain impurities or be contaminated.

Losses during separation/ purification of product

For practice in answering AS Chemistry questions, why not use *Collins Exam Practice AS Chemistry*?

# CALCULATING THEORETICAL YIELD

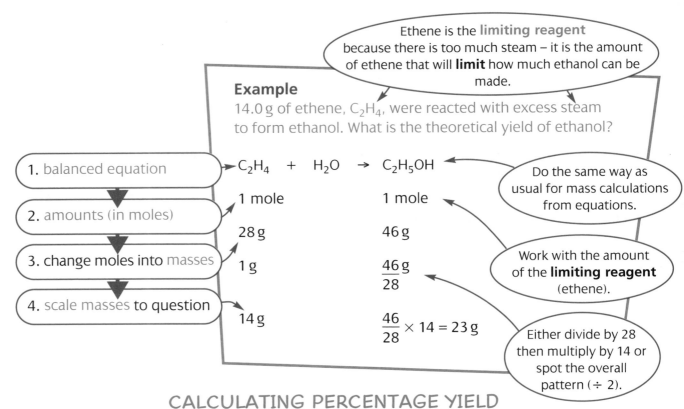

Ethene is the **limiting reagent** because there is too much steam – it is the amount of ethene that will **limit** how much ethanol can be made.

**Example**

14.0 g of ethene, $C_2H_4$, were reacted with excess steam to form ethanol. What is the theoretical yield of ethanol?

1. balanced equation

2. amounts (in moles)

3. change moles into masses

4. scale masses to question

$$C_2H_4 \ + \ H_2O \ \rightarrow \ C_2H_5OH$$

|  |  |
|---|---|
| 1 mole | 1 mole |
| 28 g | 46 g |
| 1 g | $\dfrac{46}{28}$ g |
| 14 g | $\dfrac{46}{28} \times 14 = 23$ g |

Do the same way as usual for mass calculations from equations.

Work with the amount of the **limiting reagent** (ethene).

Either divide by 28 then multiply by 14 or spot the overall pattern (÷ 2).

# CALCULATING PERCENTAGE YIELD

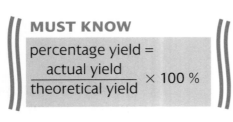

**MUST KNOW**

percentage yield = $\dfrac{\text{actual yield}}{\text{theoretical yield}} \times 100 \%$

**Example**

The actual yield of ethanol in the experiment above was 17.0 g. What is the percentage yield?

$$\text{percentage yield} \ = \ \frac{\text{actual yield}}{\text{theoretical yield}} \times 100\%$$

$$= \frac{17}{23} \times 100 = 73.9\%$$

**WORKED EXAMPLE**

This reaction takes place during the manufacture of sulphuric acid.

$$SO_2 + \tfrac{1}{2}O_2 \rightleftharpoons SO_3$$

(a) Calculate the percentage yield when 0.6 tonnes of sulphur trioxide are made from 1 tonne of sulphur dioxide reacting with excess oxygen.

(b) Suggest a reason why the yield cannot reach 100%.

(a) Theoretical yield

| (equation) | $SO_2$ | + | $\tfrac{1}{2}O_2$ | $\rightleftharpoons$ | $SO_3$ |
|---|---|---|---|---|---|
| (moles) | 1 mole | | | | 1 mole |
| (masses) | 64 g | | | | 80 g |
| (scale) | 64 tonnes | | | | 80 tonnes |
| | 1 tonne | | | | 1.25 tonnes |

The theoretical yield is **1.25 tonnes**.

Percentage yield $= \dfrac{\text{actual yield}}{\text{theoretical yield}} \times 100\%$

$$= \frac{0.6}{1.25} \times 100 = 48\%$$

The percentage yield is **48%**.

(b) This is a reversible reaction so it cannot give 100% yield.

# GAS VOLUME CALCULATIONS

## GAS VOLUMES

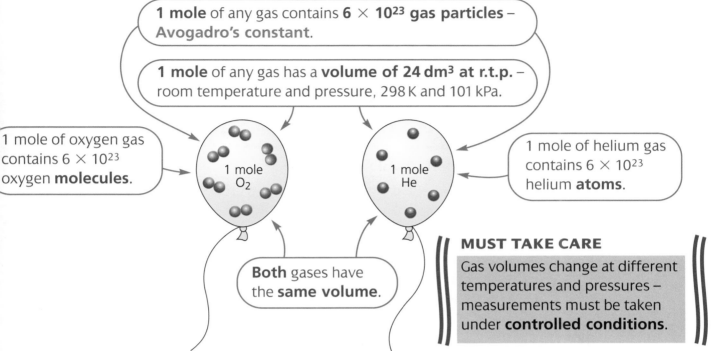

**1 mole** of any gas contains **6 × 10²³ gas particles** – Avogadro's constant.

**1 mole** of any gas has a **volume of 24 dm³ at r.t.p.** – room temperature and pressure, 298 K and 101 kPa.

1 mole of oxygen gas contains 6 × 10²³ oxygen **molecules**.

1 mole O₂

1 mole He

1 mole of helium gas contains 6 × 10²³ helium **atoms**.

**Both** gases have the **same volume**.

**MUST TAKE CARE**

Gas volumes change at different temperatures and pressures – measurements must be taken under **controlled conditions**.

start
Edexcel only

## THE IDEAL GAS LAW

The ideal gas law is used to calculate the volume of a gas at different temperatures and pressures.

**pressure** in pascals (Pa)

**R** is the **gas constant** (= 8.31 J K⁻¹ mol⁻¹)

**volume** in cubic metres (m³)

$$pV = nRT$$

**number of moles** of gas

**temperature** in kelvin (K)

**UNITS**

The gas constant R is defined in **SI units** (J K⁻¹ mol⁻¹). This means that the other terms in the ideal gas law must be converted to SI units as well: m³, Pa and K.

Conversions:   1 m³ = 1000 dm³ = 10⁶ cm³
1000 Pa = 1 kPa
T in K = T in °C + 273

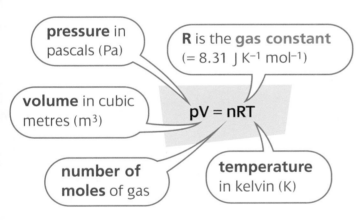

**WORKED EXAMPLE**

How many moles of methane gas are contained in a flask of volume 0.5 m³ at 100 kPa pressure and 90°C?

(convert to SI)   p = 100 kPa = 100 × 10³ Pa
V = 0.5 m³
n = unknown
R = 8.31 J K⁻¹ mol⁻¹
T = 90°C = 273 + 90 = 363 K

(rearrange and substitute)   $pV = nRT$, gives $n = \dfrac{pV}{RT}$

(work out)   $n = \dfrac{100 \times 10^3 \times 0.5}{8.31 \times 363} = 16.58$ moles

end
Edexcel only

# CALCULATING GAS VOLUMES FROM EQUATIONS

> Use the same basic method as for mass calculations!

Four steps for working out reacting volumes:

> Step 1: write a **balanced equation**

> Step 2: write the **amounts (in moles)** of the substances in the question

> Remember to use **shortcut** if the question is only about gases!

> Step 3: change moles into **masses and/or volumes** → Step 4: **scale** to the question

## Calculations involving gases only

What volume of oxygen is needed for the complete combustion of 10 cm³ of hydrogen (at r.t.p.)?

1. equation

2. moles

3. volumes

4. scale

$$2H_2 \quad + \quad O_2 \quad \rightarrow \quad 2H_2O$$

2 moles     1 mole

2 volumes    1 volume

10 cm³     **5 cm³**

> **Shortcut!** If 2 moles (48 dm³) react with 1 mole (24 dm³) then twice the volume of hydrogen reacts to any volume of oxygen.

## Calculations mixing masses and volumes

What is the maximum volume of hydrogen that can be made when 1.0 g of magnesium reacts with excess dilute hydrochloric acid (at r.t.p.)?

1. equation

2. moles

3. masses and volumes

4. scale

$$Mg \quad + \quad 2HCl \quad \rightarrow \quad MgCl_2 \quad + \quad H_2$$

1 mole            1 mole

24 g             24 dm³

1.0 g          $\frac{24}{24} = \textbf{1 dm}^3$

> The question gives **mass** for magnesium, but asks for **volume** of hydrogen – this time the shortcut won't work.

---

**WORKED EXAMPLE**

(a) What volume of oxygen is needed for the complete combustion of 50 cm³ methane?

(b) How would the total volume change before and after the reaction? All measurements are taken at r.t.p.

(a) (equation)    $CH_4(g) \quad + \quad 2O_2(g) \quad \rightarrow \quad CO_2(g) \quad + \quad 2H_2O(l)$
      (moles)       1 mole       2 moles       (1 mole)      (liquid – very small volume)
      (volumes)    1 volume     2 volumes
      (scale)       50 cm³      **100 cm³**

(b) The volume would be less after the reaction. There are three moles of gas on the left-hand side and only one mole (carbon dioxide) on the right-hand side. Water is a liquid and so has a very small volume.

# CONCENTRATION CALCULATIONS

## MAKING UP SOLUTIONS

To make up a solution of known concentration:

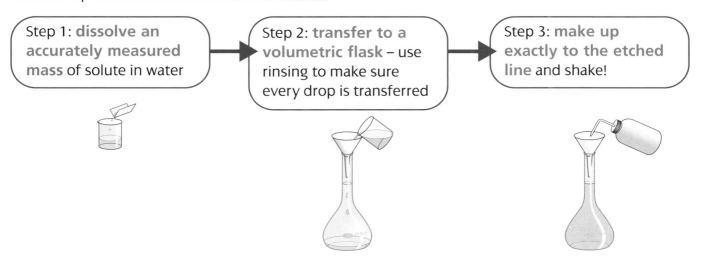

Step 1: **dissolve an accurately measured mass** of solute in water

Step 2: **transfer to a volumetric flask** – use rinsing to make sure every drop is transferred

Step 3: **make up exactly to the etched line** and shake!

## WORKING OUT CONCENTRATIONS

**Concentrations** are usually given in:

- **g dm⁻³** (grams per cubic decimetre)   or   • **mol dm⁻³** (moles per cubic decimetre).

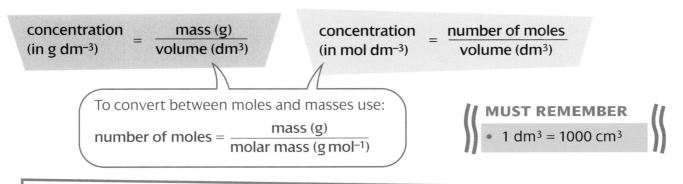

$$\text{concentration (in g dm}^{-3}) = \frac{\text{mass (g)}}{\text{volume (dm}^3)}$$

$$\text{concentration (in mol dm}^{-3}) = \frac{\text{number of moles}}{\text{volume (dm}^3)}$$

To convert between moles and masses use:

$$\text{number of moles} = \frac{\text{mass (g)}}{\text{molar mass (g mol}^{-1})}$$

**MUST REMEMBER**

- $1 \text{ dm}^3 = 1000 \text{ cm}^3$

**Examples**

What mass of sodium hydroxide is needed to make 500 cm³ of 0.5 mol dm⁻³ solution?

*The question gives information in moles so work in moles first.*

number of moles needed = 0.5 in 1 dm³ = 0.25 in 500 cm³

mass = number of moles × molar mass = 0.25 × 40 = 10 g

*Now convert to mass.*

What is the concentration, in mol dm⁻³, of a solution containing 5.0 g of sodium hydroxide in 250 cm³ of solution?

*The question gives information about mass so work in mass first.*

$$\text{concentration (in g dm}^{-3}) = \frac{5.0}{250 \times 10^{-3}}$$
$$= 20 \text{ g dm}^{-3}$$

*250 cm³ = 250 × 10⁻³ dm³*

$$\text{number of moles} = \frac{\text{mass (g)}}{\text{molar mass (g mol}^{-1})} = \frac{20}{40} = 0.5 \text{ mol}$$

*Now convert to moles.*

so concentration (in mol dm⁻³) = 0.5 mol dm⁻³

# TITRATION CALCULATIONS

## WHICH RESULTS TO USE?

- Use only accurate results (1, 2 and 4).
- Ignore 'roughs' and any obviously inaccurate 'outliers' (3).
- Take an average of the 'accurates' (1, 2 and 4) to use in calculations.

Results/cm³

| Rough | 1 | 2 | 3 | 4 |
|-------|------|------|------|------|
| 25.0 | 24.1 | 24.3 | 25.1 | 24.2 |

## CALCULATING CONCENTRATIONS

25.0 cm³ of 0.2 mol dm⁻³ sodium hydroxide was placed in a flask and titrated with a solution of dilute hydrochloric acid. The average titration value was 26.1 cm³ of dilute hydrochloric acid.
What is the concentration of hydrochloric acid?

**Step 1: write a balanced equation**

$$NaOH \ + \ HCl \ \rightarrow \ NaCl \ + \ H_2O$$

**Step 2: write down the amounts (in moles)**

1 mole                    1 mole

This is a rearrangement of **concentration** $= \dfrac{\textbf{number of moles}}{\textbf{volume (dm}^3\textbf{)}}$

**Step 3: work out the amount (in moles) of the 'known' solution in the flask**

no. of moles of 'known' NaOH = concentration × volume
= 0.2 × 25 × 10⁻³ = 5 ×10⁻³ moles

**Work in dm³:**
25 cm³ = 25 × 10⁻³ dm³

**Step 4: work out the concentration of the 'unknown' in the burette**

concentration of HCl $= \dfrac{5 \times 10^{-3}}{26.1 \times 10^{-3}}$
= 0.19 mol dm⁻³

- Look at Step 2:
  no. moles NaOH = no. moles HCl
- Then use equation:
  concentration = $\dfrac{\text{number of moles}}{\text{volume (dm}^3\text{)}}$

## WORKED EXAMPLE

25 cm³ nitric acid was placed in a flask. A titration was carried out using 0.5 mol dm⁻³ sodium hydroxide.
These are the titration results.

|  | Rough | 1 | 2 | 3 | 4 |
|---|------|------|------|------|------|
| End burette reading (cm³) | 13.00 | 12.50 | 24.50 | 36.95 | 49.40 |
| Start burette reading (cm³) | 0.00 | 0.00 | 12.50 | 24.50 | 36.95 |
| Volume of NaOH used (cm³) |  |  |  |  |  |

(a) Work out the volume of NaOH used during each titration.
(b) Calculate the average titration value.

(a)

|  | Rough | 1 | 2 | 3 | 4 |
|---|------|------|------|------|------|
| Volume of NaOH used (cm³) | 13.00 | 12.50 | 12.00 | 12.45 | 12.45 |

(b) Average: Use only titrations 1, 3 and 4.
$\dfrac{12.50 + 12.45 + 12.45}{3} = 12.47$ cm³

Ignore the 'rough', and ignore titration 2. This value 12.00 is an 'outlier' because it is not very close to the other titration values.

# IONIC COMPOUNDS

## IONIC BONDING

- **Ions** are formed when atoms **gain or lose electrons**.
- **Metals** lose electrons to form positive ions – **cations**.
- **Non-metals** gain electrons to form negative ions – **anions**.
- Ions are stable when they have **noble gas electronic configurations**.
- An ionic bond is the **electrostatic attraction** between positive and negative ions.

**IONIC BONDING IN SODIUM CHLORIDE**

**One electron** is transferred from sodium to chlorine.

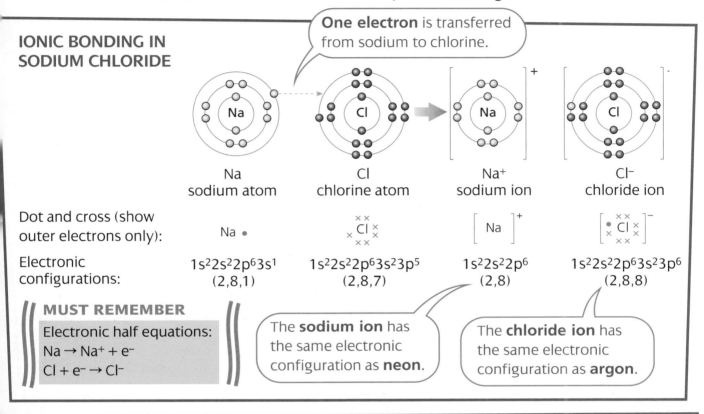

| Na<br>sodium atom | Cl<br>chlorine atom | Na⁺<br>sodium ion | Cl⁻<br>chloride ion |

Dot and cross (show outer electrons only):

Na •   $\times^{\times}_{\times} Cl^{\times}_{\times}$   $\left[ \text{Na} \right]^{+}$   $\left[ \bullet^{\times}_{\times} Cl^{\times}_{\times} \right]^{-}$

Electronic configurations:

$1s^2 2s^2 2p^6 3s^1$ (2,8,1)   $1s^2 2s^2 2p^6 3s^2 3p^5$ (2,8,7)   $1s^2 2s^2 2p^6$ (2,8)   $1s^2 2s^2 2p^6 3s^2 3p^6$ (2,8,8)

**MUST REMEMBER**

Electronic half equations:
$Na \rightarrow Na^+ + e^-$
$Cl + e^- \rightarrow Cl^-$

The **sodium ion** has the same electronic configuration as **neon**.

The **chloride ion** has the same electronic configuration as **argon**.

**IONIC BONDING IN MAGNESIUM OXIDE**

**Two electrons** are transferred from magnesium to oxygen.

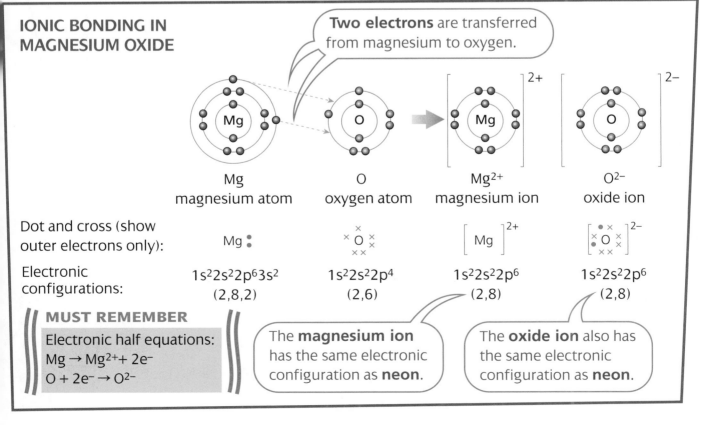

| Mg<br>magnesium atom | O<br>oxygen atom | Mg²⁺<br>magnesium ion | O²⁻<br>oxide ion |

Dot and cross (show outer electrons only):

Mg **:**   $\times^{\times}_{\times} O^{\times}_{\times}$   $\left[ \text{Mg} \right]^{2+}$   $\left[ \bullet^{\times}_{\bullet} O^{\times}_{\times} \right]^{2-}$

Electronic configurations:

$1s^2 2s^2 2p^6 3s^2$ (2,8,2)   $1s^2 2s^2 2p^4$ (2,6)   $1s^2 2s^2 2p^6$ (2,8)   $1s^2 2s^2 2p^6$ (2,8)

**MUST REMEMBER**

Electronic half equations:
$Mg \rightarrow Mg^{2+} + 2e^-$
$O + 2e^- \rightarrow O^{2-}$

The **magnesium ion** has the same electronic configuration as **neon**.

The **oxide ion** also has the same electronic configuration as **neon**.

# WORKING OUT THE FORMULAE FOR IONIC COMPOUNDS

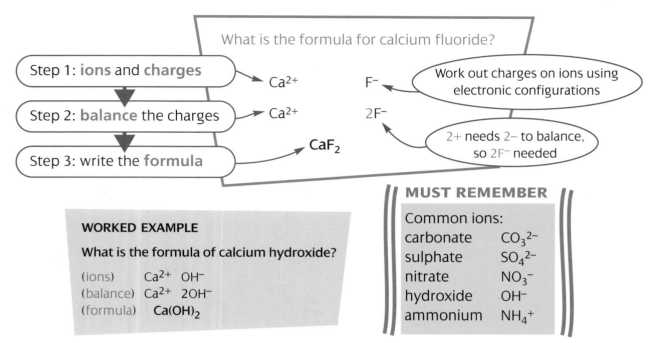

What is the formula for calcium fluoride?

Step 1: **ions** and **charges** → $Ca^{2+}$   $F^-$ ← Work out charges on ions using electronic configurations

Step 2: **balance** the charges → $Ca^{2+}$   $2F^-$ ← 2+ needs 2− to balance, so $2F^-$ needed

Step 3: write the **formula** → $CaF_2$

**WORKED EXAMPLE**

What is the formula of calcium hydroxide?

(ions)    $Ca^{2+}$  $OH^-$
(balance) $Ca^{2+}$  $2OH^-$
(formula)  $Ca(OH)_2$

**MUST REMEMBER**

Common ions:
carbonate    $CO_3^{2-}$
sulphate     $SO_4^{2-}$
nitrate      $NO_3^-$
hydroxide    $OH^-$
ammonium     $NH_4^+$

# ELECTRON AFFINITIES

start
Edexcel only

- **Ionisation energies** give information about the energy changes when atoms form positive ions (see page 5).
- **Electron affinities** give information about the energy changes when atoms form negative ions.

The first electron affinity is defined as the energy change when one mole of gaseous atoms accepts one mole of electrons to form one mole of ions with a single negative charge.

For example:   $Cl(g) + e^- \rightarrow Cl^-(g)$

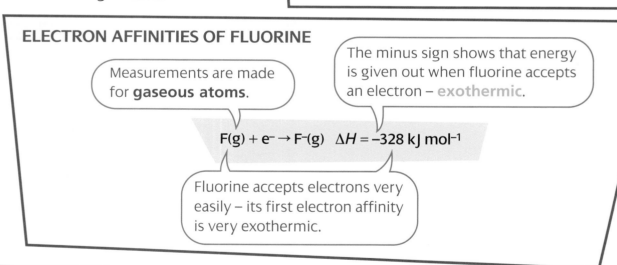

## ELECTRON AFFINITIES OF FLUORINE

Measurements are made for **gaseous atoms**.

The minus sign shows that energy is given out when fluorine accepts an electron – **exothermic**.

$$F(g) + e^- \rightarrow F^-(g) \quad \Delta H = -328 \text{ kJ mol}^{-1}$$

Fluorine accepts electrons very easily – its first electron affinity is very exothermic.

## SECOND ELECTRON AFFINITIES

**The second electron affinity is defined as the energy needed to be taken in to add a second electron to an atom.**

Second electron affinities are always **endothermic**. The atom already has an 'extra' electron so the second one is repelled by the extra negative charge.

For example:
$$O^-(g) + e^- \rightarrow O^{2-} \quad \Delta H = +798 \text{ kJ mol}^{-1}$$

end
Edexcel only

# COVALENT COMPOUNDS

## COVALENT BONDING

- Atoms in **covalent compounds** gain noble gas electron configurations by sharing electrons.
- A single covalent bond is **two electrons** shared between two atoms – a bonding pair.
- Most atoms (except hydrogen) share electrons to form a **stable octet** – 8 outer shell electrons.
- Covalent compounds usually (not always!) contain compounds that have 3 to 5 electrons in their outer shell – too many to lose or gain to form ions.
- Compounds of carbon are all covalently bonded (except for carbonates).

---

### ELEMENT WITH SINGLE BOND

**For example: hydrogen**

Two shared electrons = **single bond**

$$H \bullet \quad \times H \longrightarrow H \overset{\bullet}{\underset{\times}{}} H \qquad H—H$$

hydrogen atoms     hydrogen molecule, $H_2$    displayed formula

Each hydrogen atom has 2 electrons in its outer shell – the same as the noble gas helium.

- The 2 shared electrons in the hydrogen molecule form a single covalent bond.
- These electrons form a **bonding pair**.

---

### COMPOUND WITH SINGLE BOND

**For example: water**

Show outer electrons only.

Notice the **lone pairs** or **non-bonding pairs** around oxygen.

Hydrogen has the same noble gas configuration as helium; oxygen (2,8) is the same as neon.

$$H \bullet \qquad H \bullet \qquad \times \overset{\times \times}{\underset{\times \times}{O}} \times \longrightarrow H \overset{\times \times}{\underset{\times \times}{\overset{\bullet}{\underset{\bullet}{O}}}} \times H$$

hydrogen atoms     oxygen atom     water molecule, $H_2O$    displayed formula

Notice that:
- Oxygen shares electrons to gain a stable octet – 8 outer shell electrons.
- A water molecule has two single bonds – bonding pairs.
- The oxygen has 4 other outer shell electrons – two **lone pairs** (sometimes called non-bonding pairs).

**MUST TAKE CARE**

Don't forget to show **ALL** outer shell electrons – not just bonding pairs!

---

### WORKED EXAMPLE

Draw dot and cross diagrams for the following molecules – show outer shell electrons only.
(a) chlorine, $Cl_2$
(b) hydrogen chloride, HCl

Only outer shell electrons shown

(a)    Cl atom      $Cl_2$      (b)   H and Cl atoms     HCl

Remember:
- Only show the outer shell electrons.
- Include the lone (non-bonding) pairs around the Cl.
- Check that H has two outer shell electrons and other atoms have an octet (8).

# MORE COVALENT BONDS

## COMPOUND WITH DOUBLE BOND

**For example: carbon dioxide**

Each double bond has **4 electrons**.

$O = C = O$

carbon dioxide
molecule, $CO_2$

displayed
formula

Notice that:

- A **double bond** contains two bonding pairs.
- All atoms have stable octets – 8 outer shell electrons.
- Oxygen has two lone pairs – non-bonding pairs.

## ION WITH DATIVE BOND

**For example: ammonium ion**

The electrons in the bond both come from the **lone pair** on the nitrogen atom – this is a **dative bond**.

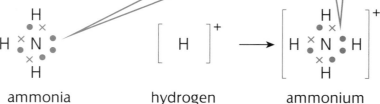

ammonia
molecule

hydrogen
ion

ammonium
ion, $NH^{4+}$

displayed
formula

This is a **charged ion** but the bonding that holds the atoms together is **covalent**.

- A **dative bond** forms when both bonding electrons come from one atom.
- Atoms need **lone pairs** – non-bonding pairs – to form dative bonds.

### WORKED EXAMPLE

**Draw dot and cross diagrams to show the following molecules.**
(a) oxygen, $O_2$
(b) ethene, $C_2H_4$

(a)

O atom          $O_2$

Remember to do the 'octet' check!

(b)

C atom   H atom          $C_2H_4$

# SHAPES OF MOLECULES

## ELECTRON PAIR REPULSION

Groups of electrons in a molecule:

- repel each other and move as far apart as possible
- may be **bonding pairs** – in single, double or triple bonds
- may be **lone pairs** (non-bonding pairs) – not involved in bonding.

**MUST KNOW**

- The **shapes** and **bond angles** in molecules with **between 2 and 6 atoms** around the central atom.

## BASIC SHAPES

### SHAPES OF MOLECULES CONTAINING NO LONE PAIRS

| | Number of atoms around central atom | Dot and cross | Bond angles | Shape |
|---|---|---|---|---|
| **Beryllium chloride** <br> Formula: $BeCl_2$ | 2 | | 180° <br> Cl — Be — Cl | Linear |
| **Carbon dioxide** <br> Formula: $CO_2$ | 2 | | 180° <br> O = C = O | Linear |
| **Boron trichloride** <br> Formula: $BCl_3$ | 3 | | 120°   120° <br> Cl — B — Cl <br> 120° | Trigonal planar |

The double bonds act as single electron groups.

---

**WORKED EXAMPLE**

Explain why the carbon dioxide molecule has a linear shape.

The central C atom is surrounded by **two double bonds**.

Four shared electrons are involved in each double bond, leading to a very high **electron density**.

The two double bonds repel each other, so move as far apart as possible, creating a **linear molecule** with a **bond angle of 180°**.

## MOLECULES WITH MORE ATOMS

| Number of atoms around central atom | Dot and cross | Bond angles | Shape |
|---|---|---|---|
| 4 e.g. $CH_4$ | | $109.5°$ | Tetrahedral |
| 5 e.g. $PCl_5$ | | $90°$ $120°$ | Trigonal bipyramidal |
| 6 e.g. $SF_6$ | | | Octahedral |

## SHAPES OF MOLECULES WITH LONE PAIRS

- Electrons in lone pairs, as well as electrons in bonds, affect the shape of the molecule.

- Molecules with lone pairs are often 'bent'.

- Molecules with lone pairs usually have bond angles less than the 'standard shapes' shown above.

**MUST REMEMBER**

- bonding pair–bonding pair
- bonding pair–lone pair
- lone pair–lone pair

greater repulsion

**Ammonia**

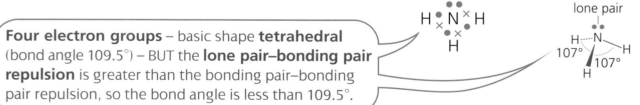

lone pair

$107°$ $107°$

**Four electron groups** – basic shape **tetrahedral** (bond angle 109.5°) – BUT the **lone pair–bonding pair repulsion** is greater than the bonding pair–bonding pair repulsion, so the bond angle is less than 109.5°.

## WORKED EXAMPLE

Draw a diagram to show the shape of a water molecule.
Explain why the molecule has this shape.

$104.5°$

There are **four electron groups** so the basic shape is **tetrahedral** (bond angle 109.5°). However, the **lone pair–lone pair repulsion** is very great, so the bond angle is even smaller (104.5°).

# POLAR COVALENT BONDS

## ELECTRONEGATIVITY

**Electronegativity is defined as the power of an atom to attract electrons towards itself in a covalent bond.**

- The **electronegativity** of elements in the Periodic Table:
  - increases across a period (from left to right)
  - decreases down a group.
- **Polar molecules** have small positive ($\delta+$) and negative charges ($\delta-$) due to differences in the electronegativities of atoms bonded together.

## EXAMPLES OF POLAR MOLECULES

### HYDROGEN CHLORIDE

This is a polar molecule because the electronegativity of chlorine is greater than hydrogen.

The **uneven sharing** of electrons gives H a **small positive charge ($\delta+$)** and Cl a **small negative charge ($\delta-$)**.

$$\overset{\delta+}{H} \underset{\times \,\bullet}{\text{——}} \overset{\delta-}{Cl}$$

Electro-negativity: **2.1**   **3.0**

Cl has a **higher electronegativity** so it pulls the electrons in the bond **closer**.

---

### OTHER EXAMPLES

C and H have very similar electronegativities – the C–H bond is **not polar**.

|  | Electronegativity values |
|---|---|
| H | 2.1 |
| C | 2.5 |
| O | 3.5 |
| F | 4.0 |

Fluorine is the most electronegative element.

In larger molecules, look for a **polar bond** to decide whether the molecule is polar.

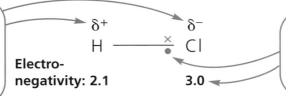

Fluoromethane is polar because F is **more electronegative** than H or C.

## NON-POLAR MOLECULES

In symmetrical molecules, electronegativity differences cancel out so the molecule is not polar.

$CCl_4$ is **not polar** because the $\delta-$ charges **cancel out**.

The **charges do not cancel out** in ammonia because the molecule is **not symmetrical**.

**MUST TAKE CARE**

Watch out for lone pairs like the one on the nitrogen atom in ammonia – charges don't always cancel out in molecules with lone pairs!

# CHARGE POLARISATION IN IONIC COMPOUNDS

- Some **ionic bonds** show partial covalent character due to **polarisation**.
- Polarisation happens when a **cation** – a positive ion – pulls the electrons in the charge cloud of an anion closer to itself.

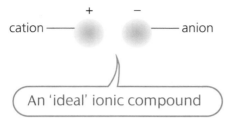

cation —— anion

An 'ideal' ionic compound

The cation is **polarising** the electrons from the anion towards itself – the bond is not 'purely ionic' because the electrons are no longer completely transferred.

- The **polarising power** of a **cation** is **higher** when:
  - it has a **high charge** – $Al^{3+}$ is more polarising than $Na^+$
  - it is **smaller** – ions get bigger 'down the group' in the Periodic Table.

  Small + positive = high
  ion    charge     charge   density
  
  Small ion + high positive charge = high charge density

- **An anion** is **more easily polarised** when:
  - it has a higher charge
  - it is **larger** – the extra electrons are less tightly held by the nucleus.

  Large ion + high negative charge = low charge density

## IONIC VERSUS COVALENT

—— electrons more evenly shared ——→

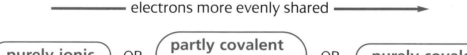

Compounds can be: **purely ionic** OR **partly covalent and partly ionic** OR **purely covalent**

$$\left[ Na \right]^+ \quad \left[ \overset{\times}{\underset{\bullet\bullet}{Cl}} \right]^- \qquad \overset{\delta+}{H} - Cl^{\delta-} \qquad Cl - Cl$$

←—— electrons more completely transferred ——

## MOLECULAR ORBITALS

start
Edexcel only

**An orbital is an area of space where an electron is most likely to be found.**

- When atoms form molecules, the **s and p atomic orbitals** form **sigma (σ)** and **pi (π) molecular orbitals** respectively.

H  H  ⟶  H—H

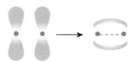

**For example:** 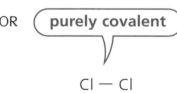  O=O   O=O

s orbitals overlap to form a σ molecular orbital

p orbitals overlap to form a π molecular orbital

oxygen has a double bond: (σ and π orbitals)

end
Edexcel only

For practice in answering AS Chemistry questions, why not use *Collins Exam Practice AS Chemistry*?

# INTERMOLECULAR FORCES

intermolecular forces = imfs

- **Simple covalent molecules** contain small groups of atoms – e.g. water, $H_2O$.
- Simple covalent compounds have low melting and boiling points.
- **Intermolecular forces (imfs)** are attractions between simple covalent molecules.
- imfs are very weak compared to covalent or ionic bonds.
- There are three types of imfs:
  - **induced dipole–induced dipole** – van der Waals
  - **permanent dipole–permanent dipole**
  - **hydrogen bonding**.

## PERMANENT DIPOLE–PERMANENT DIPOLE FORCES

- **Permanent dipole forces** happen between **polar molecules**.
- Permanent dipole forces give compounds higher boiling points.

### Oxygen

$O{=}O$

$M_r = 32$
Boiling point $-183°C$

### Hydrogen chloride

$\delta^+ \quad \delta^- \qquad \delta^+ \quad \delta^-$
$H{-}Cl$ ---------- $H{-}Cl$

$M_r = 36.5$
Boiling point $-85°C$

The $\delta+$ and $\delta-$ charges **increase the forces of attraction** between HCl molecules.

- HCl has a permanent dipole:
  - due to the difference in electronegativity between H and Cl.
- The permanent dipole forces:
  - cause HCl to have a much higher boiling point than $O_2$.

- $O_2$ is a non-polar molecule so:
  - no permanent dipole forces
  - no attraction between molecules.
- As $O_2$ doesn't have a permanent dipole:
  - its boiling point is much lower than HCl
  - even though the two molecules have similar molar mass.

**MUST TAKE CARE**

Permanent dipole forces are weak attractions – the boiling point is still very low!

**WORKED EXAMPLE**

Which of the following molecules has the higher boiling point? Explain your reasoning.
$CCl_4$    $CHCl_3$

$CHCl_3$ has a higher boiling point.
$CCl_4$ is a symmetrical, non-polar molecule with induced dipole–induced dipole forces between molecules.
$CHCl_3$ is non-symmetrical and so is polar.

The forces between molecules are permanent dipole–permanent dipole, which are stronger than induced dipole forces, so the boiling point is higher.

**MUST CHECK**

'Shapes of molecules', page 25, and 'Polar covalent bonds', page 27.

# INDUCED DIPOLE FORCES

Simple molecules without permanent dipoles gain **induced dipoles** when they are close to other polar molecules.

$$\underset{\text{non-polar } Cl_2}{Cl-Cl} \qquad \overset{\delta+ \quad\;\; \delta-}{\underset{\substack{\text{polar HCl attracts electrons in } Cl_2 \\ \text{and induces a dipole}}}{H-Cl}} \longrightarrow \overset{\delta+ \quad\; \delta- \quad \delta+ \qquad\; \delta-}{\underset{\substack{\text{permanent dipole–} \\ \text{induced dipole force}}}{Cl-Cl \; \text{-----} \; H-Cl}}$$

---

Non-polar atoms and molecules can also gain an instantaneous (temporary) dipole because the electrons are always moving around, so at any one instant may happen to be more at one end of the atom/molecule than at the other.

**For example: noble gases**

$$\overset{\delta+ \qquad \delta-}{\underset{\substack{\text{A dipole on} \\ \text{this atom}}}{Xe}} \qquad \underset{\text{induces}}{} \qquad \underset{\substack{\text{a dipole on} \\ \text{the next.}}}{Xe} \longrightarrow \overset{\delta+ \quad\;\; \delta- \quad \delta+ \qquad \delta-}{\underset{\substack{\text{This causes a very weak} \\ \textbf{induced dipole–} \\ \textbf{induced dipole force}}}{Xe \; \text{-----} \; Xe}}$$

---

## MUST REMEMBER

- **Bigger atoms** have **stronger induced dipole forces** because there are more electron shells, so there is a **bigger electron 'cloud'** that can be polarised more easily.
- The **boiling points** of the noble gases **increase down the group** as the atoms get larger.
- Induced dipole forces are the **weakest** type of **intermolecular force**.

## MUST KNOW

Different books use different terms so must remember that these all mean the same thing:
- induced dipole–induced dipole
- temporary dipole–temporary dipole
- instantaneous dipole–induced dipole
- van der Waals forces

---

### WORKED EXAMPLE

Put the following molecules in order of increasing boiling point.
Explain your reasoning.
HCl    CH$_4$    C$_2$H$_6$

$$\underset{\text{Increasing boiling point}}{\underrightarrow{CH_4 \quad C_2H_6 \quad HCl}}$$

HCl has the **highest boiling point** because it is a **polar molecule** and so has the strongest intermolecular forces (**permanent dipole–permanent dipole**).
CH$_4$ and C$_2$H$_6$ are **non-polar molecules** and so have **induced dipole forces** between molecules. C$_2$H$_6$ is a larger molecule than CH$_4$ therefore it has a **larger electron cloud** that can be **more easily polarised**. This means that the induced dipole forces are **stronger** between C$_2$H$_6$ molecules. Therefore C$_2$H$_6$ has a **higher boiling point** than CH$_4$.

# MORE ABOUT INTERMOLECULAR FORCES

## HYDROGEN BONDING

- **Hydrogen bonding** happens in molecules that have an H atom bonded to a very electronegative atom with a lone pair e.g. O, F or N.

- The electronegativity difference causes the bond to be polar.

$$-O^{\delta-} \diagdown_{H^{\delta+}} \quad \text{polar bond}$$

- The $\delta+$ charge on the H atom is attracted to the lone pair on the $\delta-$ O atom of the next molecule (see 'Hydrogen bonding in water', below).

- The molecules line up, all held together by hydrogen bonds.

- Hydrogen bonding is the strongest intermolecular force.

---

## HYDROGEN BONDING IN WATER

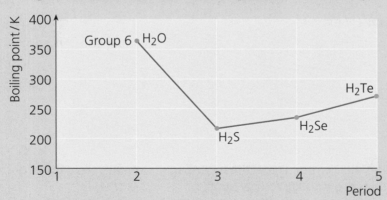

water molecule

Hydrogen bonding in water:

- is very strong compared to other imfs
- causes water to have a much higher melting point and boiling point than other molecules of similar size and mass
- causes ice – solid water – to be less dense than liquid water because the molecules are held further apart in a lattice of hydrogen bonds – some of these break on melting.

---

**WORKED EXAMPLE**

This graph shows the pattern of boiling points in Group 6 hydrides.

(Graph: Boiling point / K vs Period. Group 6 • $H_2O$ at period 2 ~365 K, $H_2S$ at period 3 ~212 K, $H_2Se$ at period 4 ~232 K, $H_2Te$ at period 5 ~271 K. Y-axis marked 150, 200, 250, 300, 350, 400. X-axis Period 1–5.)

**Explain briefly why water has a higher boiling point than the other hydrides.**

Oxygen is much more electronegative than the other Group 6 elements. This means that the O–H bond in water is very polar and hydrogen bonds form between water molecules. The other Group 6 elements are less electronegative, there is little bond polarity and no hydrogen bonds form – the main intermolecular forces are van der Waals (induced dipole forces). Hydrogen bonds are much stronger so the boiling point of water is much higher.

# INTERMOLECULAR FORCES AND CHANGES OF STATE

| Change of state | Molecular description |
|---|---|
| Melting | • **In the solid**, molecules are held in place in a lattice by imfs. |
| $\delta^+ \delta^-$ $\delta^+ \delta^-$ → $\delta^+ \delta^-$ $\delta^-$ $\delta^+$ $\delta^+$ $\delta^+ \delta^-$ $\delta^-$ solid liquid | • imfs must be **partially broken** to allow the molecules to **move over each other** in the liquid state. • imfs still keep molecules close together in the liquid state. • The covalent bonding within the molecule **is not broken** when the solid melts or boils. |
| Boiling | • imfs in the liquid hold the molecules close together. |
| $\delta^+ \delta^-$ $\delta^-$ $\delta^+$ $\delta^-$ → $\delta^+ \delta^-$ $\delta^- \delta^+$ $\delta^+ \delta^-$ $\delta^-$ $\delta^+$ liquid gas $\delta^-$ | • These must be **completely broken** so that the molecules **separate** to form a gas. • Completely separating molecules requires a **high energy input** – boiling requires more energy than melting. |

## MUST REMEMBER

- **Bonds in the molecule DO NOT BREAK** during state changes – only intermolecular forces do!
- Breaking imfs **requires energy** – endothermic.
- The **stronger the imf**, the **greater the energy** needed, the **higher the melting point** and **boiling point**.

## STRENGTHS OF INTERMOLECULAR FORCES

induced dipole–
induced dipole

permanent dipole–
induced dipole

permanent dipole–
permanent dipole

hydrogen bonding

strength of force increases
melting point increases
boiling point increases

## MUST REMEMBER

- All imfs are much weaker than covalent or ionic bonds.

## WORKED EXAMPLE

Explain the trend in boiling point of the following substances.

| | Boiling point/°C |
|---|---|
| He | −269 |
| Xe | −108 |
| HCl | −85 |
| NH₃ | −33 |

Higher boiling points are due to **stronger imfs** between atoms or molecules which need **more energy** to overcome.

He and Xe have the lowest boiling point because they are atoms **with induced dipole forces** between them. These are the **weakest** imf.

Xenon has a higher boiling point than helium because it is a larger atom with **more electron shells**.

HCl has a **permanent dipole**, so has a higher boiling point due to **permanent dipole forces**.

NH₃ has the highest boiling point of all because it contains **hydrogen bonding**, the **strongest** imf.

# STRUCTURE AND PROPERTIES

## METALLIC BONDING

A **metal** contains a regular arrangement of positive metal ions in a 'sea' of delocalised electrons.

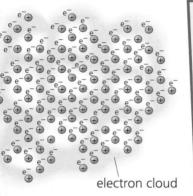

electron cloud

*Use this property to identify metals.*

### PROPERTIES OF METALS

Metals:

| | | |
|---|---|---|
| • have **high melting points and boiling points** | ...because... | the attraction between positive ions and delocalised electrons is strong – **bonding is strong**. |
| • can be worked into **different shapes** | ...because... | the **layers of metal ions can move** over each other when the metal changes shape. |
| • have **high densities** | ...because... | the metal ions are **packed close together**. |
| • are good electrical conductors | ...because... | **electrons** are delocalised and **can flow**. |

## IONIC STRUCTURE

**Ionic compounds** consist of a giant, three-dimensional lattice containing many ions.

**Example:
sodium chloride, NaCl**

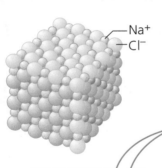

Na⁺
Cl⁻

*These properties help to identify ionic structures.*

### PROPERTIES OF IONIC COMPOUNDS

Ionic compounds:

| | | |
|---|---|---|
| • have **high melting points and boiling points** | ...because... | the electrostatic attraction between positive and negative ions is strong – **bonding is strong – large amounts of energy** are needed to overcome the attractive forces. |
| • are often soluble in water | ...because... | **charged ions** interact with the permanent dipoles of water molecules. |
| • are often crystalline | ...because... | ions are arranged in regular arrangements. |
| • conduct electricity in the **molten** and **aqueous** state, but **not as solids** | ...because... | the ions carry charge when they move – ions cannot move in solids, but can when molten or in solution. |

## SIMPLE MOLECULAR STRUCTURES

**Simple molecular structures** contain simple molecules with covalent bonding.

**Example: iodine, I₂**

*se this property to identify mple molecular structures.*

*Simple covalent molecules are **not usually soluble in water**, but molecules with **permanent dipoles** are often **soluble**.*

### PROPERTIES OF SIMPLE COVALENT ELEMENTS AND COMPOUNDS

Simple covalent elements and compounds:

| | | |
|---|---|---|
| • have very low melting points and boiling points | ...because... | there are only weak intermolecular forces (imfs) between molecules. |
| • **do not conduct electricity** | ...because... | bonding involves shared electrons so there are no charged particles. |
| • have **very low densities** | ...because... | they are usually gases or liquids due to their weak imfs. |

# GIANT MOLECULAR STRUCTURES

**Giant molecular structures:**

- contain **many atoms** covalently bonded together in a three-dimensional lattice
- can be **elements** – e.g. diamond – or **compounds** – e.g. silicon dioxide.

## Diamond

Each carbon atom in diamond is bonded to four others.

These properties help to identify giant covalent structures.

### PROPERTIES OF DIAMOND

Diamond:

| | | |
|---|---|---|
| • has a **high melting point and boiling point** | ...because... | the **covalent bonds** between atoms **are very strong** – large amounts of energy are needed to overcome the attractive forces. |
| • is **insoluble in water** | ...because... | there are **no charges** to interact with the polar water molecules. |
| • is **very hard** | ...because... | each atom is **strongly bonded to four others** in a very strong structure. |
| • **does not conduct electricity** in any state | ...because... | the bonds are formed by **shared electrons** – no charge can move through the structure. |

## Graphite

weak induced dipole-induced dipole force between layers

layer of graphite

delocalized electrons free to move

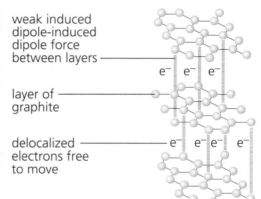

### PROPERTIES OF GRAPHITE

Graphite is a **different giant structure** – an **allotrope** – of carbon.

Graphite is an unusual giant molecular structure because:

- The **delocalised electrons** between layers allow it to **conduct electricity**.
- The bonding **within** layers is strong but **between** layers imfs are weak:
  – Layers break off easily.
  – It is stronger in one direction than the other.

### WORKED EXAMPLE

Look at the table of properties of four compounds, A, B, C and D.

| Compound | Melting point / °C | Boiling point / °C | Electrical conductivity (solid) | Solubility in water |
|---|---|---|---|---|
| A | −182 | −161 | poor | insoluble |
| B | 847 | 1527 | poor | very soluble |
| C | 180 | 1327 | very good | reacts with water |
| D | 1610 | 2230 | poor | insoluble |

Identify the type of structure of each compound.

**A** is **simple molecular** (evidence: very low melting point and boiling point).
**B** is **giant ionic** (evidence: high melting point and boiling point, and very soluble in water).
**C** is **metallic** (evidence: conducts electricity in solid state – relatively low melting point and reactivity with water suggest that C is a Group 1 element).
**D** is **giant molecular** (evidence: high melting point and boiling point and insoluble in water).

# PATTERNS IN THE PERIODIC TABLE

## ARRANGEMENTS OF ELEMENTS

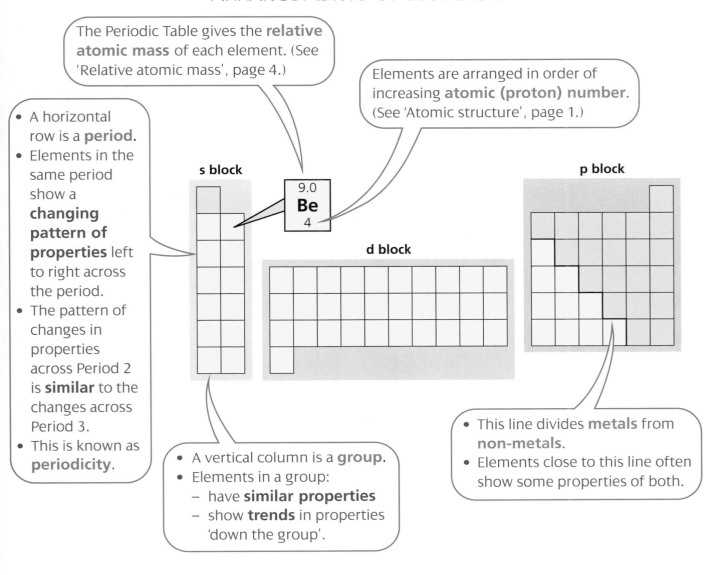

The Periodic Table gives the **relative atomic mass** of each element. (See 'Relative atomic mass', page 4.)

Elements are arranged in order of increasing **atomic (proton) number**. (See 'Atomic structure', page 1.)

- A horizontal row is a **period**.
- Elements in the same period show a **changing pattern of properties** left to right across the period.
- The pattern of changes in properties across Period 2 is **similar** to the changes across Period 3.
- This is known as **periodicity**.

**s block**

9.0
**Be**
4

**d block**

**p block**

- A vertical column is a **group**.
- Elements in a group:
  - have **similar properties**
  - show **trends** in properties 'down the group'.

- This line divides **metals** from **non-metals**.
- Elements close to this line often show some properties of both.

## ELECTRON CONFIGURATIONS

**s block**, **p block** and **d block** are named because they show which electron orbital is last to be filled – see this by writing the **electron configuration**.

**MUST REMEMBER**

- The 4s subshell has a **lower energy level** than the 3d – it fills first (see 'Electron configurations', page 7).

**For example:**

| s block | |
|---|---|
| Group **1** | Na: $1s^2 2s^2 2p^6 \mathbf{3s^1}$ |
| Group **2** | Be: $1s^2 \mathbf{2s^2}$ |

| d block | |
|---|---|
| Fe: $1s^2 2s^2 2p^6 3s^2 3p^6 \mathbf{3d^6} 4s^2$ |
| Zn: $1s^2 2s^2 2p^6 3s^2 3p^6 \mathbf{3d^{10}} 4s^2$ |

| p block | |
|---|---|
| Group **6** | O: $1s^2 2s^2 \mathbf{2p^4}$ |
| Group **7** | Cl: $1s^2 2s^2 2p^6 3s^2 \mathbf{3p^5}$ |

**s orbital** is last to fill.

**d orbital** fills **after** 4s.

**p orbital** is last to fill.

For **Groups 1 to 7**, the group number matches the **total number of electrons in the outer shell**.

# TRENDS IN ELECTRON CONFIGURATIONS

## DOWN A GROUP: GROUP 2

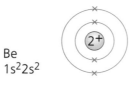

Be
$1s^22s^2$

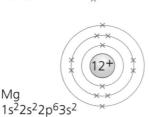

Mg
$1s^22s^22p^63s^2$

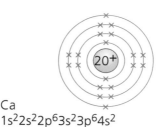

Ca
$1s^22s^22p^63s^23p^64s^2$

Down a group:
- The number of protons (positive charge on nucleus) and number of electrons increase.
- There are **more inner electron shells**.
- Inner shells **shield** the outer electrons from **positive charge** on the nucleus.
- This means there is **less attractive force** between nucleus and outer electrons.

Therefore

**Atomic radius increases** down a group – the atoms get **larger**.

**First ionisation energy decreases** down a group – less energy is needed to remove an electron to make a positive ion.

**Electronegativity decreases** down a group – there is less attraction for covalent bond electrons because the nuclear charge is **shielded**.

## ACROSS A PERIOD: PERIOD 3

Group 1

Na
$1s^22s^22p^63s^1$

Group 3

Al
$1s^22s^22p^63s^23p^1$

Group 5

P
$1s^22s^22p^63s^23p^3$

Group 0

Ar
$1s^22s^22p^63s^23p^6$

Across a period:
- Number of protons (positive charge on nucleus) and the number of electrons increase.
- Extra electrons all enter the **same shell** – e.g. in Period 3, it is shell 3 that is being filled.
- There is an **increase in the positive charge** on the nucleus but **no increase in electron shielding**.

Therefore

**Atomic radius decreases** across a period – the atoms get **smaller**.

**First ionisation energy** generally **increases** across a period – more energy is needed to remove an electron to make a positive ion.

**Electronegativity increases** across a period – there is more attraction for covalent bond electrons because the nuclear charge increases with **no increase in shielding**.

### MUST REMEMBER
- Ideas about nuclear charge and shielding explain trends in:
  – **atomic radius**
  – **ionisation energy** (see page 5)
  – **electronegativity** (see page 27 and page 41).

### MUST REMEMBER
- There are **'steps'** in the pattern of ionisation energies due to **subshells** (see page 6).

### WORKED EXAMPLE

**Explain why the atomic radius of a sodium atom is smaller than that of potassium, but larger than that of magnesium.**

Electron configurations: Na: $1s^22s^22p^63s^1$; K: $1s^22s^22p^63s^23p^64s^1$; Mg: $1s^22s^22p^63s^2$
Sodium is smaller than potassium because it has fewer electron shells. Although potassium has a larger nuclear charge (+19 compared to +11), the third inner electron shell shields the outer electrons so the attraction between the nucleus and the outer electrons is reduced making it a larger atom.
Magnesium has a higher nuclear charge (+12) than sodium but the same number of shells. This means that there is no increase in shielding by the inner electrons. The electrons in the outer shell are attracted more strongly, reducing the atomic radius.

# GROUPS 1 AND 2

## PHYSICAL PROPERTIES

**Group 1:**
- have **very low melting points** for metals
- are **soft** – can be cut with a knife.

**Group 2:**
- are **harder** and have **higher melting points** than Group 1.

| Element | Atomic number | Common oxidation state | Melting point / °C |
|---------|---------------|------------------------|--------------------|
| Li | 3 | +1 | 180 |
| Na | 11 | +1 | 98 |
| K | 19 | +1 | 63 |
| Rb | 37 | +1 | 39 |
| Cs | 55 | +1 | 29 |

| Element | Atomic number | Common oxidation state | Melting point / °C |
|---------|---------------|------------------------|--------------------|
| Be | 4 | +2 | 1278 |
| Mg | 12 | +2 | 651 |
| Ca | 20 | +2 | 850 |
| Sr | 38 | +2 | 770 |
| Ba | 56 | +2 | 704 |

Key points for both groups:

- Elements have **typical metal properties** – they all **conduct electricity** and **form positive ions**.
- **Melting points decrease** down the group – but notice the 'dip' for Mg.
- **Atomic radius increases** down the group (see page 36).
- **First ionisation energies decrease** down the group (see page 36).

start Edexcel only

## REACTIONS OF GROUP 1

**Key points: reactions with air/oxygen**
- All Group 1 elements form **ionic metal oxides**.
- All burn **very vigorously** in oxygen.
- Reactions are **faster** down the group.
- **Reactions are faster** than with Group 2 elements of the same period.
- A **complex mixture** of products is formed, e.g.
  - **oxides** such as $Na_2O$
  - **peroxides**, $K_2O_2$
  - **superoxides**, $CsO_2$

**Key points: reactions with water**
- All react to form an **aqueous metal hydroxide** and **hydrogen** gas.
- The reactions are **very exothermic** – the hydrogen often bursts into flames.
- Reactions are **faster** down the group.

Lithium reacts with water to form alkaline lithium hydroxide and hydrogen:

$$2Li(s) + 2H_2O(l) \rightarrow 2LiOH(aq) + H_2(g)$$

end Edexcel only

# REACTIONS OF GROUPS I AND 2

## Group 2 metals with air/oxygen

Magnesium burns in air with a brilliant white flame.

$$2Mg(s) + O_2(g) \rightarrow 2MgO(s)$$

Key points:
- All Group 2 metals **tarnish** in air.
- All **burn vigorously** when heated in air or oxygen.
- All form **ionic metal oxides** when they react with oxygen.

## Group 2 metals with water

Calcium reacts with water to form hydrogen and calcium hydroxide.

$$Ca(s) + 2H_2O(l) \rightarrow Ca(OH)_2(aq) + H_2(g)$$

Key points:
- Be and Mg **do not react** with cold water – Mg reacts with **hot steam**.
- Metals form **hydrogen** and a **metal hydroxide** when they react with water.
- **Rate of reaction increases** down the group.
- Group 2 hydroxides are **alkaline** – **pH increases** during the reaction.

### Key points for both Group 1 and Group 2
- **Reactions are faster** down the group.
- During the reactions the metal is **oxidised** by losing electrons to form **metal ions**.
- **Increased reactivity** is linked to **decrease in ionisation energy** down the group – it takes less energy for metal atoms to form metal ions.

**WORKED EXAMPLE**

A small piece of calcium is added to water containing Universal Indicator solution. A thermometer is used to follow the temperature change during the reaction.
**Describe and explain what you see during the reaction.**

The temperature increases because the reaction between calcium and water is exothermic.
Bubbles form due to hydrogen gas being produced. The indicator turns blue as an alkaline solution of calcium hydroxide forms. A precipitate would also form as calcium hydroxide is not very soluble in water.

# FLAME TESTS

start
Edexcel only

Different metal ions give **different flame colours** because:
- Metal cations in an ionic compound are **excited** – by strong heating.
- **Electrons** move to **higher energy levels**.
- Electrons **fall back down**, emitting energy.
- Energy emitted by different ions has **different wavelengths**.
- Different wavelengths of visible light have **different colours**.

## FLAME COLOURS

| Cation | Flame colour |
|---|---|
| Li$^+$ | deep red |
| Na$^+$ | strong yellow |
| K$^+$ | lilac |
| Be$^{2+}$ / Mg$^{2+}$ | no colour |
| Ca$^{2+}$ | brick red |
| Ba$^{2+}$ | apple green |

end
Edexcel only

# MORE GROUP 2 REACTIONS

## THERMAL DECOMPOSITION OF CALCIUM CARBONATE

Calcium carbonate is the main compound in **limestone**. Limestone is used to make 'lime' products for making building materials and to treat acid soils.

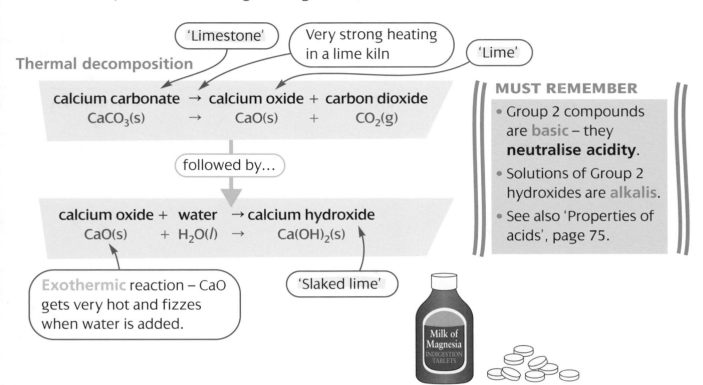

**Thermal decomposition**

'Limestone'  Very strong heating in a lime kiln  'Lime'

calcium carbonate  →  calcium oxide  +  carbon dioxide
$$CaCO_3(s) \rightarrow CaO(s) + CO_2(g)$$

followed by...

calcium oxide  +  water  → calcium hydroxide
$$CaO(s) + H_2O(l) \rightarrow Ca(OH)_2(s)$$

**Exothermic** reaction – CaO gets very hot and fizzes when water is added.

'Slaked lime'

**MUST REMEMBER**
- Group 2 compounds are **basic** – they **neutralise acidity**.
- Solutions of Group 2 hydroxides are **alkalis**.
- See also 'Properties of acids', page 75.

Milk of Magnesia
INDIGESTION TABLETS

Magnesium hydroxide is used in medicines to neutralise excess stomach acid

## THERMAL STABILITIES OF OTHER GROUP 2 CARBONATES

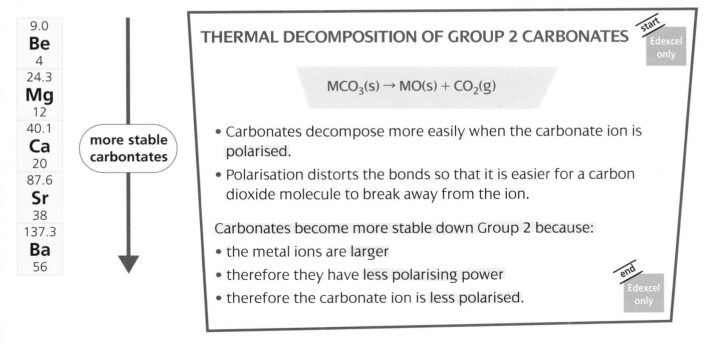

| 9.0 |
| **Be** |
| 4 |
| 24.3 |
| **Mg** |
| 12 |
| 40.1 |
| **Ca** |
| 20 |
| 87.6 |
| **Sr** |
| 38 |
| 137.3 |
| **Ba** |
| 56 |

**more stable carbontates**

**THERMAL DECOMPOSITION OF GROUP 2 CARBONATES**  *start* Edexcel only

$$MCO_3(s) \rightarrow MO(s) + CO_2(g)$$

- Carbonates decompose more easily when the carbonate ion is polarised.
- Polarisation distorts the bonds so that it is easier for a carbon dioxide molecule to break away from the ion.

Carbonates become more stable down Group 2 because:
- the metal ions are larger
- therefore they have less polarising power
- therefore the carbonate ion is less polarised.  *end* Edexcel only

**MUST REMEMBER**
- Polarising power depends on the **charge** and the **size** of the ion (see page 28).

# AQUEOUS CALCIUM HYDROXIDE – LIME WATER

Aqueous calcium hydroxide – lime water – is:
- an alkali, pH 12
- used to test for **carbon dioxide**.

Carbon dioxide turns lime water cloudy . . .

calcium hydroxide + carbon dioxide → calcium carbonate + water
$$Ca(OH)_2(aq) \quad + \quad CO_2(g) \quad \rightarrow \quad CaCO_3(s) \quad + \quad H_2O(l)$$

because . . .

If more carbon dioxide is bubbled through, the solid precipitate re-dissolves . . .

**calcium carbonate** is formed – this is an insoluble white solid.

calcium hydrogen carbonate
$$because . . . \quad CaCO_3(s) \quad + \quad CO_2(g) \quad + \quad H_2O(l) \quad \rightarrow \quad Ca(HCO_3)_2(aq)$$

calcium hydrogen carbonate is formed – this dissolves in water.

**start**
not OCR

## SOLUBILITIES OF GROUP 2 COMPOUNDS

### GROUP 2 HYDROXIDES

| | Solubility/g per 100 g water | |
|---|---|---|
| Mg(OH)$_2$ | 0.0012 | sparingly soluble |
| Ca(OH)$_2$ | 0.12 | |
| Sr(OH)$_2$ | 1.0 | more soluble |
| Ba(OH)$_2$ | 3.7 | soluble |

### GROUP 2 SULPHATES

| | Solubility/g per 100 g water | |
|---|---|---|
| MgSO$_4$ | 33 | very soluble |
| CaSO$_4$ | 0.21 | |
| SrSO$_4$ | 0.013 | less soluble |
| BaSO$_4$ | 0.00024 | insoluble |

The pattern for sulphates is the **opposite** of the pattern for hydroxides.

### MUST REMEMBER

Test for sulphate ions
- Sulphate ions give a **white precipitate** with acidified barium nitrate.

### WORKED EXAMPLE

A 'barium meal' contains barium sulphate. It is swallowed by patients before they have a stomach X-ray.
Barium compounds are toxic.
(a) Explain why swallowing barium sulphate does not cause poisoning.
(b) Explain why barium sulphate is a better choice than barium hydroxide.

(a) Barium sulphate is insoluble so passes through the body without entering any body system.
(b) Barium hydroxide is much more soluble than barium sulphate so could cause poisoning if it were used.

**end**
not OCR

# TRENDS ACROSS PERIOD 3

## TRENDS IN FIRST IONISATION ENERGIES

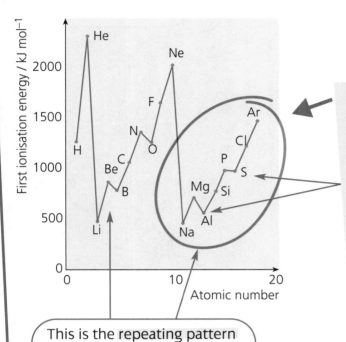

This is the **repeating pattern** for Period 2 and Period 3 – **periodicity**.

For the **first ionisation energies** for Period 3, elements Na to Ar:

- The general trend is an **increase** in ionisation energy across the period.
- The 'steps' are caused by subshells:
  - Al loses a **3p electron** first (Al: $1s^2 2s^2 2p^6 3s^2 3p^1$) – this is easier to remove than a 3s because the 3p electron is already on a **higher energy level** – hence the 'dip'.
  - Remember the p subshell contains three **p orbitals**. Phosphorus (with $3p^3$) has one electron in each p orbital.
  - Sulphur (with $3p^4$) has two electrons in one of its 3p orbitals. The repulsion of the two electrons makes it easier to lose one – hence the 'dip'.

## TRENDS IN ATOMIC RADIUS

**Atomic radius:**

- **increases** down a group
- **decreases** across a period.

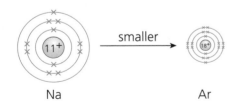

Na          Ar

## TRENDS IN ELECTRONEGATIVITY

**Electronegativity:**

- **decreases** down a group
- **increases** across a period.
- More electronegative atoms attract bonding electrons to form a **polar bond**.

$$\delta^+ \qquad \delta^-$$
$$H \overset{\times}{\underset{\bullet}{\longrightarrow}} Cl$$
$$2.1 \qquad 3.0$$

# TRENDS IN PROPERTIES RELATING TO STRUCTURE

## MUST CHECK

- Metallic bonding
- Giant molecular structures
- Simple molecular structures

on pages 33–34.

> Na, Mg and Al have **metallic bonding** – they **conduct electricity** and have **high melting and boiling points**.

> Si has a **giant covalent structure** with a **very high melting point** and **boiling point**.

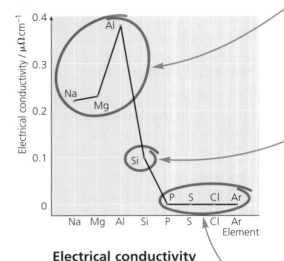

> Silicon is unusual because it is a **semiconductor**.

**Electrical conductivity**

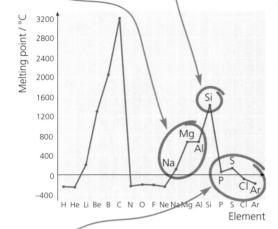

**Melting points**

> P, S, Cl and Ar have **simple covalent structures** – they **do not conduct electricity** and have **very low melting** and **boiling points**.

> These trends show **periodicity** – patterns for Periods 2 and 3 are similar.

## MUST REMEMBER

- When a **solid melts**, the forces **between particles** are broken so the particles are free to move over each other.
- **Intermolecular forces** between simple molecules – e.g. sulphur – are broken, but the **bonds in each molecule do not break**.

## WORKED EXAMPLE

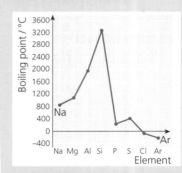

Boiling points – Period 3

Look at the graph of boiling points for the elements nitrogen to argon.
(a) Which element has the highest boiling point? Suggest a reason for this.
(b) Which element has the lowest boiling point? Suggest a reason for this.
(c) What additional information would be needed to show that this pattern was a periodic property?

(a) Silicon has the **highest boiling point**. It has a **giant molecular structure** with very strong, three-dimensional, covalent bonds which require a high energy input to break.
(b) Argon has the **lowest boiling point**. It exists as uncombined atoms. Argon atoms are the smallest in Period 3 with very **weak instantaneous dipole forces** between them. These forces can be overcome by small amounts of energy.
(c) A graph of boiling points for **Period 2 elements** would need to be used for comparison to see if the **pattern was repeated**.

# OXIDATION AND REDUCTION

## ELECTRON TRANSFER

Oxidation is Loss of electrons ── therefore... ── an **oxidiser** always accepts electrons.

**OIL RIG**

Reduction is Gain of electrons ── therefore.... ── a **reducer** always donates electrons.

**Metals**:
- **lose electrons** (are **oxidised**) in reactions and form positive ions
- **donate electrons** and so are **reducers**.
  e.g. $Mg(s) \rightarrow Mg^{2+}(s) + 2e^-$

**Non-metals**:
- **gain electrons** (are **reduced**) in reactions and form negative ions
- **accept electrons** and so are **oxidisers**.
  e.g. $O_2(g) + 4e^- \rightarrow 2O^{2-}(s)$

## WRITING HALF EQUATIONS FROM FULL EQUATIONS

**MUST REMEMBER**

- Usually:
  - electrons go on **same side** as positive ions
  - electrons go on **opposite side** to negative ions.

**RULES**

1. Use the usual charges on ions in half equations.
2. Balance half equations by adding electrons.
3. Both the numbers of atoms and charges must balance.

**Usual charges**

Group 1: 1+ e.g. $Na^+$
Group 2: 2+ e.g. $Ca^{2+}$
Group 6: 2− e.g. $O^{2-}$
Group 7: 1− e.g. $Cl^-$

Step 1: write down the **formulae** of elements and ions

Step 2: add electrons to one side to **balance charges**

Step 3: **cancel** down if possible

**Example: the reaction of sodium with chlorine**

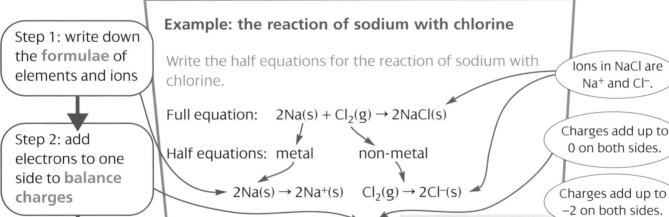

Write the half equations for the reaction of sodium with chlorine.

Full equation: $2Na(s) + Cl_2(g) \rightarrow 2NaCl(s)$

Half equations: metal          non-metal

$2Na(s) \rightarrow 2Na^+(s)$     $Cl_2(g) \rightarrow 2Cl^-(s)$

$2Na(s) \rightarrow 2Na^+(s) + 2e^-$     $Cl_2(g) + 2e^- \rightarrow 2Cl^-(s)$

$Na(s) \rightarrow Na^+(s) + e^-$

Ions in NaCl are $Na^+$ and $Cl^-$.

Charges add up to 0 on both sides.

Charges add up to −2 on both sides.

Electrons go on same side as positive ion, opposite side to negative ion.

**KEY POINTS**

1. Na is a metal in Group 1 so each atom forms an ion with a +1 charge by losing one electron – Na is oxidised.

2. Cl is a non-metal in Group 7 so each atom forms an ion with a −1 charge by gaining one electron – Cl is reduced.

# WRITING FULL EQUATIONS FROM HALF EQUATIONS

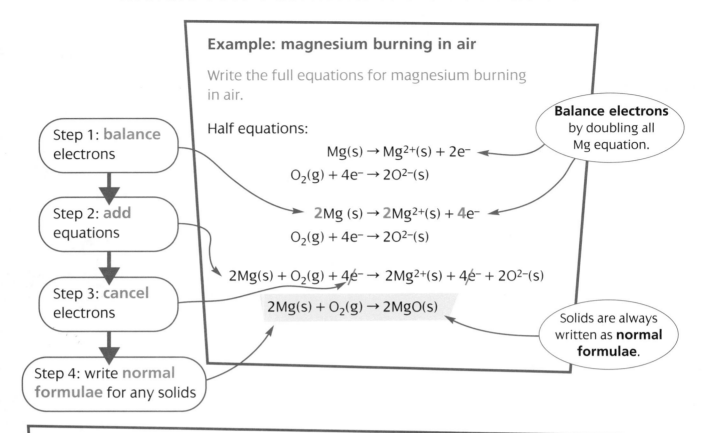

**Step 1: balance electrons**

**Step 2: add equations**

**Step 3: cancel electrons**

**Step 4: write normal formulae for any solids**

**Example: magnesium burning in air**

Write the full equations for magnesium burning in air.

Half equations:

$$Mg(s) \rightarrow Mg^{2+}(s) + 2e^-$$
$$O_2(g) + 4e^- \rightarrow 2O^{2-}(s)$$

**Balance electrons** by doubling all Mg equation.

$$2Mg(s) \rightarrow 2Mg^{2+}(s) + 4e^-$$
$$O_2(g) + 4e^- \rightarrow 2O^{2-}(s)$$

$$2Mg(s) + O_2(g) + 4e^- \rightarrow 2Mg^{2+}(s) + 4e^- + 2O^{2-}(s)$$

$$2Mg(s) + O_2(g) \rightarrow 2MgO(s)$$

Solids are always written as **normal formulae**.

## KEY POINTS

- Magnesium is a metal, it forms positive ions by losing electrons (oxidation).
- Oxygen is a non-metal, it forms negative ions by gaining electrons (reduction).
- The simple definition of oxidation as gain of oxygen works here, but does not work for all examples – e.g. look again at the sodium–chlorine reaction.

### WORKED EXAMPLE

Write the half equations for the reaction of lithium (Li) with oxygen to form lithium oxide. Then use these half equations to construct a full equation for the reaction. Which element is the reducing agent in the reaction?

**Half equations:** (note: Li is in Group 1, therefore forms ions with a 1+ charge)

(Elements and ions)            before:   Li(s)                      $O_2(g)$
                                after:    $Li^+(s)$                  $O^{2-}(s)$

(Balance electrons and atoms)          $Li(s) \rightarrow Li^+(s) + e^-$          $O_2(g) + 4e^- \rightarrow 2O^{2-}(s)$

Electrons go on same side as positive ion, opposite side to negative ion

**Full equation:**        Li(s)                      $\rightarrow Li^+(s) + e^-$
                          $O_2(g) + 4e^-$            $\rightarrow 2O^{2-}(s)$

(Balance electrons)       4Li(s)                     $\rightarrow 4Li^+(s) + 4e^-$
                          $O_2(g) + 4e^-$            $\rightarrow 2O^{2-}(s)$

Balance electrons by multiplying Li equation by 4

(Add and cancel)          $4Li(s) + O_2(g) + 4e^- \rightarrow 4Li^+(s) + 4e^- + 2O^{2-}(s)$

(Formula of solid)        $4Li(s) + O_2(g)$          $\rightarrow 2Li_2O(s)$

Ions:       $Li^+$       $O^{2-}$
Formula:    $Li_2O$

**Reducing agent:** (Reducing agent is another wording for reducer)
In the reaction, electrons are donated by lithium to oxygen, so lithium is the reducing agent.

# OXIDATION STATES

## RULES FOR WORKING OUT OXIDATION STATES

### RULES

1. The **oxidation state** of elements is always 0.
2. In compounds, the total sum of oxidation states is always 0.
3. In ions, the total sum of oxidation states equals the charge on the ion.
4. Common oxidation states in compounds:

| Group 1 | +1 |
|---------|-----|
| Group 2 | +2 |
| H | +1 (except in metal hydrides) |
| F | −1 |
| Cl | −1 (except when combined with O or F) |
| O | −2 (except in peroxides) |

## WORKING OUT OXIDATION STATES IN COMPOUNDS

**Step 1:** write down **known oxidation states**

**Step 2:** write down a **total sum** of oxidation states

**Step 3:** work out **unknown oxidation states PER ATOM**

**MUST REMEMBER**

- Oxidation state values are always given **per atom** – here there are 2 sulphur atoms, each with [Ox] = +2.

### SIMPLE IONIC COMPOUNDS

*Total oxidation states add up to zero in a compound.*

What are the oxidation states of the magnesium and chloride ions in magnesium chloride?

$$MgCl_2$$

| | |
|---|---|
| Known [Ox] | +2 −1 |
| Sum [Ox] | +2 + [2 × (−1)] = 0 |
| (As expected) | [Ox]Mg = +2   [Ox]Cl= −1 |

### OTHER IONIC COMPOUNDS

What is the oxidation state of sulphur in $MgS_2O_3$?

*Oxidation states add up to zero.*

$$MgS_2O_3$$

| | |
|---|---|
| Known [Ox] | +2 ? −2 |
| Sum [Ox] | +2 + [2 × [Ox]S] + [3 × (−2)] = 0 |
| Unknown [Ox] | 2 × [Ox]S = +4 |
| | [Ox]S = +2 |

### IONS

*Total oxidation state of the ion is the charge on the ion.*

What is the oxidation state of nitrogen in the nitrate ion $NO_3^-$?

$$NO_3^-$$

| | |
|---|---|
| Known [Ox] | ? −2 |
| Sum [Ox] | [Ox]N + [3 × (−2)] = −1 |
| Unknown [Ox] | [Ox]N = +5 |

### COVALENT COUMPOUNDS

What is the oxidation state of carbon in ethene, $C_2H_4$?

$$C_2H_4$$

| | |
|---|---|
| Known [Ox] | ? +1 |
| Sum [Ox] | 2 × [Ox]C + [4 × (+1)] = 0 |
| Unknown [Ox] | 2 × [Ox]C = −4 |
| | [Ox]C = −2 |

# REDOX REACTIONS

**Oxidation:** an element is **oxidised** when its oxidation state increases.

**Reduction:** an element is **reduced** when its oxidation state decreases.

Reduction and oxidation happen at the same time in reactions – this is known as redox.

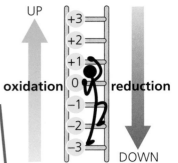

**Oxidation state**

UP
+3
+2
+1
oxidation  0  reduction
−1
−2
−3
DOWN

## LOOKING AT REDOX EQUATIONS

**Step 1:** work out the **oxidation states** of the elements in the question.

→

**Step 2:** which element **increases** its oxidation state? (Is oxidised)? This is the reducer (reducing agent).

→

**Step 3:** which element **decreases** its oxidation state? (Is reduced)? This is the oxidiser (oxidising agent).

### Example

Which element is reduced and which is oxidised during this displacement reaction?

$$Cl_2(aq) \; + \; 2KI(aq) \; \rightarrow \; I_2(aq) \; + \; 2KCl(aq)$$

$0 \qquad +1 \; -1 \qquad 0 \qquad +1 \; -1$

Oxidised element is iodine – its oxidation state has increased from −1 to 0.

Reduced element is chlorine – its oxidation state has decreased from 0 to −1.

## COMMON REDOX REACTIONS

- Reactions of the **s block metals** (Group 1 and 2 elements) with oxygen, water and acids – see pages 37, 38 and 75.
- Reactions of the **halogens** (Group 7) – see pages 49 and 50.

### MUST REMEMBER

- Always talk about **atoms** or **elements** … NOT compounds!!!
  RIGHT: 'Iodide ions are oxidised' ✓
  WRONG: 'Potassium iodide is oxidised' ✗

This answer does not show whether it is K or I that has been oxidised.

### WORKED EXAMPLE

Iron(II) chloride reacts with chlorine gas to form iron(III) chloride. Identify the oxidising and reducing agents in the reaction.

Easiest to work with **single formula** i.e. $FeCl_2$ and $FeCl_3$.

$$2FeCl_2(s) \; + \; Cl_2(g) \; \rightarrow \; 2FeCl_3(s)$$

(known)    [Ox]Fe = ? **−1**    **0**    [Ox]Fe = ? **−1**

(work out unknown)   [Ox]Fe −2 = 0    [Ox]Fe −3 = 0

[Ox]Fe = +2    [Ox]Fe = +3

On the left-hand side, the Cl have different oxidation states – make it clear which is which in the answer.

Therefore:

Fe is **oxidised** (from [Ox] +2 to +3). The oxidising agent is chlorine gas, $Cl_2$.

Cl in chlorine gas is **reduced** (from [Ox] 0 to −1). The reducing agent is Fe.

Cl in chloride ions is **unchanged** during the reaction.

# THE HALOGENS

## PHYSICAL PROPERTIES

| 19.0 |
| :---: |
| **F** |
| 9 |
| 35.5 |
| **Cl** |
| 17 |
| 79.9 |
| **Br** |
| 35 |
| 126.9 |
| **I** |
| 53 |

### KEY POINTS

- The halogens have **diatomic** (2-atom) molecules.
- They are **simple molecules**:
  - In the solid, molecules are held in place by very weak intermolecular forces.
  - These forces are induced dipole forces – also called instantaneous dipole forces or van der Waals forces.
  - Melting points and boiling points are low.
  - Bonding is covalent so halogens do not conduct electricity.

## TRENDS IN PROPERTIES

### BOILING POINTS

Chlorine is a green gas.
Bromine is a volatile orange liquid.
Iodine is a grey/purple solid.

|  | Boiling point /°C | State |
| :---: | :---: | :---: |
| $F_2$ | −188 | gas |
| $Cl_2$ | −34 | gas |
| $Br_2$ | 59 | liquid |
| $I_2$ | 187 | solid |

**larger molecules
higher boiling points
less volatile**

Boiling points increase down the group because:

- Halogen molecules gain an **instantaneous dipole** when electrons happen to be more at one end of the atom/molecule than at the other (see 'Induced dipole forces' page 30).
- The molecule is now **polarised** – it is δ+ at one end and δ– at the other.
- This **induces** other molecules to polarise.

$$\delta^+I{-}I^{\delta^-}$$

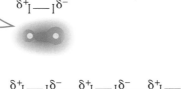

$$\delta^+I{-}I^{\delta^-}{\cdots}\delta^+I{-}I^{\delta^-}{\cdots}\delta^+I{-}I$$

induced dipole–induced dipole attraction

- The **induced dipole–induced dipole forces** hold the molecules together.
- The **stronger** the forces, the **higher** the boiling point.
- The **larger** molecules are polarised **more easily** because their electron clouds are more spread out.

### ELECTRONEGATIVITY

|  | Electronegativity |
| :---: | :---: |
| F | 4.0 |
| Cl | 3.0 |
| Br | 2.8 |
| I | 2.5 |

**decreases**

Electronegativity decreases down the group because:

- The positive charge on the nucleus is more shielded because there are more electron shells.
- This means there is less attractive force acting on the bonding electrons.

### MUST REMEMBER

- **Electronegativity** is the power of an atom to attract electrons towards itself in a covalent bond.

Fluorine is the most electronegative element on the Periodic Table.

# HALOGEN COMPOUNDS: THE HALIDES

**HALIDES**

- Halogens form **ionic halides** when they react with **metals**.
- These contain halide ions: **F⁻**, **Cl⁻**, **Br⁻**, **I⁻**.

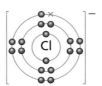

chloride ion, Cl⁻

- Metal halides are **ionic solids**.
- Examples include:
  – sodium bromide, **NaBr**
  – calcium chloride, **CaCl₂**.

- Halogens form **covalent halides** with other non-metals.

H × Cl

hydrogen chloride, HCl
(outer electrons only)

- **Hydrogen halides:**
  – have the formula HX, e.g. HF, HCl
  – are gases containing **simple covalent molecules**
  – dissolve in water to form **acidic solutions** containing ions.
- For example:
  – hydrogen chloride: $HCl(g) \rightarrow$ hydrochloric acid: $H^+(aq) + Cl^-(aq)$
  – hydrogen bromide: $HBr(g) \rightarrow$ hydrobromic acid: $H^+(aq) + Br^-(aq)$

## TESTING FOR HALIDES

**1. Silver nitrate test**
add acidified aqueous silver nitrate

THEN...

**2. Ammonia test**
add concentrated aqueous ammonia

**Results:**

| | | |
|---|---|---|
| Fluoride F⁻ | no precipitate | no further change |
| Chloride Cl⁻ | white precipitate | redissolves |
| Bromide Br⁻ | cream precipitate | redissolves |
| Iodide I⁻ | yellow precipitate | does not dissolve |

**General equation:**
$Ag^+(aq) + X^-(aq) \rightarrow AgX(s)$
(X⁻ is Cl⁻, Br⁻ or I⁻)

precipitate

**WORKED EXAMPLE**

Describe how acidified aqueous silver nitrate can be used to distinguish between aqueous potassium chloride and aqueous potassium bromide.
Write full and ionic equations for any changes that occur.

Add acidified **silver nitrate**.
Results: Potassium chloride gives a **white precipitate** of silver chloride.
Full equation: $AgNO_3(aq) + KCl(aq) \rightarrow AgCl(s) + KNO_3(aq)$
Ionic equation: $Ag^+(aq) + Cl^-(aq) \rightarrow AgCl(s)$ (K⁺ and NO₃⁻ ions are **spectator ions**)

Results: Potassium bromide gives a **cream precipitate** of silver bromide.
Full equation: $AgNO_3(aq) + KBr(aq) \rightarrow AgBr(s) + KNO_3(aq)$
Ionic equation: $Ag^+(aq) + Br^-(aq) \rightarrow AgBr(s)$

# REDOX REACTIONS OF THE HALOGENS

## OXIDISING POWER (ELEMENTS)

During reactions:

- **Halogens** act as **oxidisers** by accepting electrons to form **halide ions**.

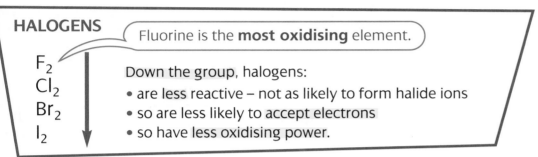

$$X_2(aq) \quad + \quad 2e^- \quad \rightarrow \quad 2X^-(aq)$$

for example: $Cl_2(aq) + 2e^- \rightarrow 2Cl^-(aq)$

- More reactive halogens – e.g. fluorine – are more likely to accept electrons to form halide compounds.

---

**HALOGENS**

Fluorine is the **most oxidising** element.

$F_2$
$Cl_2$
$Br_2$
$I_2$

Down the group, halogens:
- are less reactive – not as likely to form halide ions
- so are less likely to accept electrons
- so have less oxidising power.

---

## DISPLACEMENT REACTIONS

**MUST REMEMBER**

- A **more reactive halogen** will **displace** a **less reactive halogen** from a solution of its halide – but not the other way round!

**For example:**

Chlorine is more reactive than iodine.

Displaced halogen

BUT...

Iodine is less reactive than bromine.

chlorine + potassium iodide → potassium chloride + iodine

iodine + potassium bromide → no reaction

No displacement

| | | | | | |
|---|---|---|---|---|---|
| Full: | $Cl_2(aq)$ + | $2KI(aq)$ | → | $2KCl(aq)$ + | $I_2(aq)$ |
| Ionic: | $Cl_2(aq)$ + | $2I^-(aq)$ | → | $2Cl^-(aq)$ + | $I_2(aq)$ |
| [Ox]: | **0** | –1 | → | **–1** | 0 |

Chlorine **oxidises** iodine by accepting electrons.

---

## WHICH HALOGEN?

**Look for:**

| | |
|---|---|
| chlorine | very pale green solution |
| bromine | orange brown solution<br>hexane gives orange/red layer |
| iodine | brown solution<br>hexane gives purple layer |

Use a few drops of hexane to tell the difference between bromine and iodine.

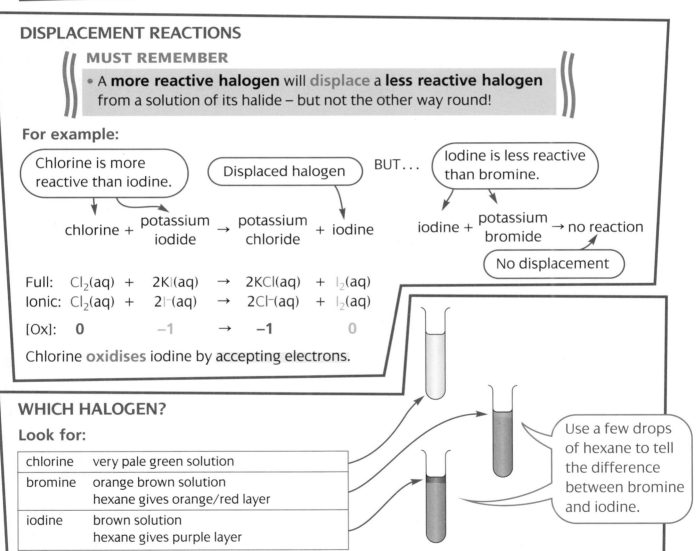

---

**WORKED EXAMPLE**

Aqueous iodine was added to potassium bromide. A brown solution was formed.
Suggest what substance causes the brown colour and outline how you would confirm this.

Iodine is **less reactive** than bromine so **cannot displace** it. The brown colour is due to (**unreacted**) **aqueous iodine**. To confirm this, add a few drops of **hexane** which will turn **purple**.

# REDUCING POWER (HALIDE IONS)

During reactions:

- **Halide ions** act as **reducers** by giving up electrons to form **halogens**.

$$2X^-(aq) \rightarrow X_2(aq) + 2e^-$$

for example: $2I^-(aq) \rightarrow I_2(aq) + 2e^-$

- Halide ions of less reactive halogens – e.g. iodide ions – are more likely to give up electrons to form halogens.

---

**HALIDE IONS**

$F^-$
$Cl^-$
$Br^-$
$I^-$

Down the group, halide ions:
- are more easily changed back into elements
- are more likely to give up electrons
- have more reducing power.

---

**REACTIONS OF HALIDES WITH CONCENTRATED SULPHURIC ACID**

conc. $H_2SO_4(l)$ +
[Ox]S= **+6**

| | | | | | | | |
|---|---|---|---|---|---|---|---|
| Na**Cl**(s) [Ox] **−1** | forms | NaHSO₄(s) **+6** | H**Cl**(g) **−1** | | | | |

$NaCl(s)$ forms $NaHSO_4(s) + HCl(g)$
[Ox] **−1** ..... **+6** ..... **−1**

$NaBr(s)$ forms $NaHSO_4(s) + SO_2(g) + HBr(g) + Br_2(g) + H_2O(l)$
[Ox] −1 ..... **+6** ..... **+4** ..... **−1** ..... 0

$NaI(s)$ forms $NaHSO_4(s) + SO_2(g) + H_2S(g) + HI(g) + I_2(g) + H_2O(l)$
[Ox] −1 ..... **+6** ..... **+4** ..... **−2** ..... **−1** ..... 0

**Sulphur** is **more reduced** by halide ion

---

**WORKED EXAMPLE**

This reaction between sodium iodide and concentrated sulphuric acid produces a mixture of products including hydrogen iodide, HI, iodine, $I_2$, sulphur dioxide, $SO_2$ and hydrogen sulphide, $H_2S$.
(a) Show how the oxidation states of sulphur and iodine change during the reaction.
(b) Explain why adding the same acid to sodium chloride does not produce chlorine.

(a) Reactants: NaI ..... $H_2SO_4$ ..... Products: HI ..... $I_2$ ..... $SO_2$ ..... $H_2S$
..... −1 ..... +6 ..... −1 ..... 0 ..... +4 ..... −2

The iodide ion is **oxidised** when it forms iodine. Sulphur in sulphuric acid is **reduced** in both products.
(b) Chloride ions are **not as powerful reducing agents** as iodide ions and cannot reduce sulphur in conc. sulphuric acid. This means that they cannot lose electrons to form chlorine.

end
Edexcel only

---

## OTHER IMPORTANT REDOX REACTIONS

**Chlorine** is added to water to kill microbes – e.g. for drinking water or in swimming pools.

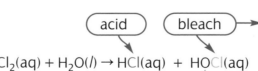

therefore, $Cl_2$ turns litmus paper red then bleaches it.

(acid) (bleach)

$$Cl_2(aq) + H_2O(l) \rightarrow HCl(aq) + HOCl(aq)$$
0 ..... −1 ..... +1

The **chlorate(I)** ion, $OCl^-$, acts as a bleach.

These are **disproportionation** reactions – chlorine is both **oxidised** and **reduced**.

Chlorine reacts with cold aqueous sodium hydroxide.

$$Cl_2(g) + 2NaOH(aq) \rightarrow NaCl(aq) + NaClO(aq) + H_2O(l)$$
0 ..... −1 ..... +1

This reaction makes **liquid bleach** for toilet cleaners.

# STANDARD ENTHALPY CHANGES

## EXOTHERMIC REACTIONS

- **Exothermic** reactions **release** heat energy to the surroundings.
- The **enthalpy change**, $\Delta H$, is always **negative**.

> EXOTHERMIC
> REACTION
> $\Delta H$ –ve

## OXIDATION REACTIONS

- Oxidation reactions are **exothermic**.
- Important **exothermic** oxidation reactions include combustion and respiration. ⟶

> Respiration releases energy
> glucose
> $C_6H_{12}O_6 + 6O_2 \rightarrow 6CO_2 + 6H_2O$

---

**Example: combustion of methane**

> Heat energy is **given out**.

$$CH_4(g) + 2O_2(g) \rightarrow CO_2(g) + 2H_2O(l) \qquad \Delta H^{\ominus}_{298} = -890 \text{ kJ mol}^{-1}$$

> Exothermic reactions are **not always spontaneous**.
> Methane and oxygen need **activation energy** from a burning flame before they start reacting.

> $\Delta H$ **is negative** – it is an **exothermic** reaction.

---

## ENDOTHERMIC REACTIONS

- **Endothermic** reactions **take in** heat energy from the surroundings.
- The **enthalpy change**, $\Delta H$, is always **positive**.

> ENDOTHERMIC
> REACTION
> $\Delta H$ +ve

### THERMAL DECOMPOSITION AND PHOTOSYNTHESIS

- Important **endothermic** reactions include thermal decomposition and photosynthesis. ⟶

> Photosynthesis is the reverse process to respiration
> $6CO_2 + 6H_2O \rightarrow C_6H_{12}O_6 + 6O_2$

---

**Example: thermal decomposition of calcium carbonate (limestone)**

> Heat energy is **taken in**.

$$CaCO_3(s) \rightarrow CaO(s) + CO_2(g) \qquad \Delta H^{\ominus}_{298} = +179 \text{ kJ mol}^{-1}$$

> Limestone must be **heated very strongly** to provide energy for the reaction.

> $\Delta H$ **is positive** – it is an **endothermic** reaction.

# ENTHALPY CHANGES UNDER STANDARD CONDITIONS

This symbol shows that the enthalpy change is measured under **standard conditions**.

Standard conditions are:
- 100 kPa pressure – 'normal' 1 atm pressure
- a stated temperature, usually 298K (= room temperature, 25°C).

Measurements are made **per mole** of stated equation – in this case 1 mol of $H_2$ burns and 1 mol of $H_2O$ is made.

$$H_2(g) + \tfrac{1}{2}O_2(g) \rightarrow H_2O(l)$$

$$\Delta H^{\ominus}_{298} = -286 \text{ kJ mol}^{-1}$$

This means that equations must have **state symbols**.

Standard conditions includes **standard states** for the reactants and products.

## IMPORTANT ENTHALPY CHANGE DEFINITIONS

All definitions mention:
- one mole
- standard conditions (298K, 100 kPa)
- all reactants and products in their **standard states**.

The standard enthalpy change of combustion
$$\Delta H^{\ominus}_c$$
is the enthalpy change when one mole of a substance burns completely in oxygen under standard conditions.

The standard enthalpy change of formation
$$\Delta H^{\ominus}_f$$
is the enthalpy change when one mole of a compound is formed from its elements under standard conditions.

The standard enthalpy change of neutralisation
$$\Delta H^{\ominus}_{neut}$$
is the enthalpy change when an acid and a base react to form one mole of water under standard conditions.

**WORKED EXAMPLE**

(a) Write the equation for the standard enthalpy change of combustion of ethane, $C_2H_6$ ($\Delta H = -1560$ kJ mol$^{-1}$).

Balanced equation:
$2C_2H_6(g) + 7O_2(g) \rightarrow 4CO_2(g) + 6H_2O(l)$
Enthalpy change of combustion equation:
$C_2H_6(g) + 3\tfrac{1}{2}O_2(g) \rightarrow 2CO_2(g) + 3H_2O(l)$  $\Delta H^{\ominus}_{298} = -1560$ kJ mol$^{-1}$

Write the equation for **one mole** and show **state symbols**.

(b) Under what conditions is the value of the enthalpy change measured?

The value is measured at 298K and 100 kPa pressure.

(c) Water is released as a hot gas during combustion. Comment on the state symbol for water in the equation.

All reactants and products are in their standard states – the standard state of water is a liquid.

# ENTHALPY PROFILE DIAGRAMS

## HOW TO DRAW ENTHALPY PROFILE DIAGRAMS

### EXOTHERMIC REACTIONS ($\Delta H$ NEGATIVE)

1. Draw the reactants on a higher energy level than the products.

2. Remember heat energy is given out during the reaction.

3. The products have less energy than the reactants.

**MUST REMEMBER**

- In **chemical reactions**, energy is usually taken in or given out as **heat energy**.

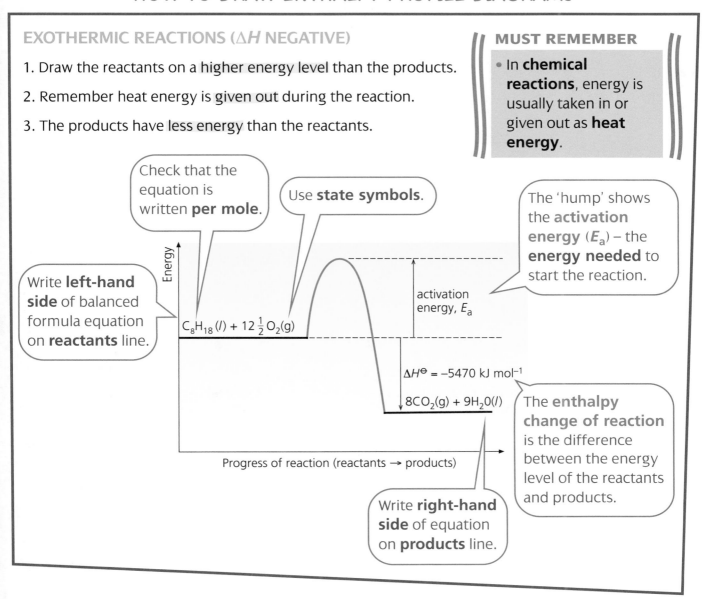

Check that the equation is written **per mole**.

Use **state symbols**.

The 'hump' shows the **activation energy** ($E_a$) – the **energy needed** to start the reaction.

Write **left-hand side** of balanced formula equation on **reactants** line.

$C_8H_{18}(l) + 12\frac{1}{2}O_2(g)$

activation energy, $E_a$

$\Delta H^\ominus = -5470 \text{ kJ mol}^{-1}$

$8CO_2(g) + 9H_2O(l)$

The **enthalpy change of reaction** is the difference between the energy level of the reactants and products.

Progress of reaction (reactants → products)

Write **right-hand side** of equation on **products** line.

## WHAT IS ACTIVATION ENERGY?

- Even exothermic reactions do not always happen spontaneously.

- Activation energy is the energy needed to start a reaction.

$E_a$

- For example, energy from a match or a spark may start a combustion reaction.

- Activation energy provides energy to break bonds.

- If molecules collide without enough activation energy, they do not react.

# ENDOTHERMIC REACTIONS ($\Delta H$ POSITIVE)

1. Draw the reactants on a lower energy level than the products.

2. Remember heat energy is taken in during the reaction.

3. The products have more energy than the reactants.

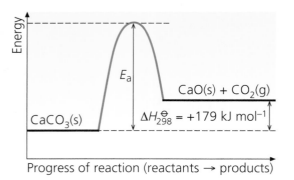

The activation energy ($E_a$) for an **endothermic reaction** is measured from the energy level of the **reactants**.

## WORKED EXAMPLE

The standard enthalpy change of formation of sodium chloride is given as
$\Delta H_f^\ominus = -411$ kJ mol$^{-1}$
Draw an enthalpy level diagram to show the profile for the formation of sodium chloride.
Label the activation energy.

Equation: $Na(s) + \frac{1}{2}Cl_2(g) \longrightarrow NaCl(s)$ $\Delta H_f^\ominus = -411$ kJ mol$^{-1}$

## MUST TAKE CARE

- Make sure that **heads of arrows** end in the **right place**.
- If the arrow is drawn carelessly short, the examiner may not give a mark.

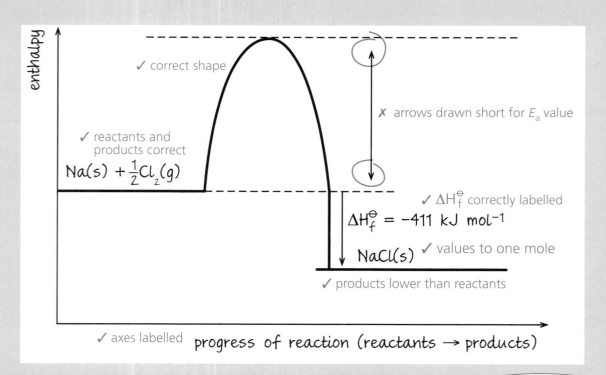

✓ correct shape

✗ arrows drawn short for $E_a$ value

✓ reactants and products correct

$Na(s) + \frac{1}{2}Cl_2(g)$

✓ $\Delta H_f^\ominus$ correctly labelled

$\Delta H_f^\ominus = -411$ kJ mol$^{-1}$

$NaCl(s)$ ✓ values to one mole

✓ products lower than reactants

✓ axes labelled progress of reaction (reactants → products)

$\Delta H_f$ values are to form **one mole of compound**

# BOND ENTHALPIES

## BREAKING BONDS

**Bond Enthalpy, $E$, is the energy required to break one mole of a particular type of bond in gaseous molecules under standard conditions – 298K, 100 kPa.**

The energy per bond is very small – **one mole** of bonds is an easier value to work with.

**Each type of bond**, e.g. H–H or C–H, has a **different bond enthalpy**.

Notice the **'one mole'** under **'standard conditions'** again!

## BOND ENTHALPY VALUES

**Key points**

- Values are all positive.
- This means that bond enthalpies are **endothermic**.
- i.e. breaking bonds uses/takes in energy.

| Bond | $E(X–Y)/$ $kJ\ mol^{-1}$ |
|---|---|
| C—C | +347 |
| C=C | +612 |
| C≡C | +838 |
| C—H | +413 |
| C—O | +358 |
| C=O (in $CO_2$) | +805 |
| H—H | +436 |
| O—H | +464 |
| O=O | +498 |

- The values are **averages** for each type of bond.
- The same bond may have **very slightly different** bond enthalpies in **different compounds**.

$$H — O — H$$

$$H — \overset{\overset{\displaystyle H}{|}}{\underset{\underset{\displaystyle H}{|}}{C}} — O — H$$

- The O–H bond has a slightly different enthalpy value.

## WHAT ABOUT MAKING BONDS?

- When a particular bond is broken, energy is taken in (endothermic).
- For example:
  H–H(g) → H(g) + H(g)  $\Delta H = \mathbf{+}$ 436 kJ mol$^{-1}$

- When the same bond is made, energy is given out (exothermic).
  H(g) + H(g) → H–H(g)  $\Delta H = \mathbf{-}$ 436 kJ mol$^{-1}$

The amount of energy is the **same**.

During reactions different bonds are **broken** and made.

H–H(g) + $\frac{1}{2}$O=O(g) → H–O–H(g) $\Delta H$ = −286 kJ mol$^{-1}$    H–O–H(g) → H–H(g) + $\frac{1}{2}$O=O(g) $\Delta H$ = +286 kJ mol$^{-1}$

## COMMON EXAM QUESTIONS

**WORKED EXAMPLE**

Explain why the reaction of hydrogen with oxygen is exothermic.

Energy is **taken in to break the bonds** in the reactants (hydrogen and oxygen). ✔ **Energy is given out when the bonds are formed** in the products (water). ✔ **More energy is given out** when the bonds are formed **than is taken in** therefore the overall reaction is **exothermic**. ✔

Use the **names** of the actual reactants and products from the question.

3 key points ✔✔✔ in each answer!

**WORKED EXAMPLE**

Explain why the reaction that produces hydrogen and oxygen from water is endothermic.

Energy is **taken in to break the bonds** in the reactants (water). ✔ **Energy is given out when the bonds are formed** in the products (hydrogen and oxygen). ✔ **Less energy is given out** when the bonds are formed **than is taken in** therefore the overall reaction is **endothermic**. ✔

# CALCULATING ENTHALPY CHANGES OF REACTION FROM BOND ENTHALPIES

**Step 1:** use the **equation** for the reaction to **list the numbers** of **each type of bond** in the reactants and products

**Step 2:** work out how much energy is **needed** to **break every bond** in the reactants ($E_1$)

**Step 4:** **add them together** to get the total energy change of reaction ($E_1 + E_2$)

### Example

Calculate the enthalpy change of reaction when 1 mole of methane, $CH_4$, burns completely to form carbon dioxide and water.

$$CH_4(g) + 2O_2(g) \rightarrow CO_2(g) + 2H_2O(g)$$

$4 \times$ C–H bonds    $2 \times$ O=O bonds    $2 \times$ C=O bonds    $4 \times$ O–H bonds

| Reactant bonds | Energy needed to break bonds / kJ mol⁻¹ | Product bonds | Energy given out when bonds form / kJ mol⁻¹ |
|---|---|---|---|
| $4 \times$ C–H | $4 \times +413 = +1652$ | $2 \times$ C=O | $2 \times -805 = -1610$ |
| $2 \times$ O=O | $2 \times +498 = +996$ | $4 \times$ O–H | $4 \times -464 = -1856$ |
| **Total energy needed** | $= +2648$ | **Total energy given out** | $= -3466$ |

**Enthalpy change of reaction = +2648 + (–3466) = –818 kJ mol⁻¹**

Don't forget the signs:
+ for bond breaking
– for bond making

**Step 3:** work out how much energy is **given out** to **form every bond** in the products ($E_2$)

## BOND ENTHALPIES AND ENTHALPY LEVEL DIAGRAMS

The same information can be shown on an **enthalpy level diagram**.

Breaking all the bonds gives **single, gaseous atoms**.

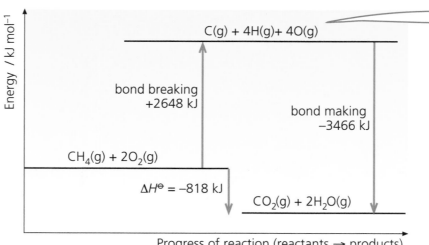

Progress of reaction (reactants → products)

---

**WORKED EXAMPLE**

The value for the enthalpy change of combustion of methane is $\Delta H_c^\ominus = -890$ kJ mol⁻¹.
Explain why this value differs from the value calculated above.

**Bond enthalpy values** are for molecules in their **gaseous states. Enthalpy change of combustion** is measured from substances in their **standard states**. The standard state for water is liquid. The difference between the two values for this reaction is due to the enthalpy change when water changes from a liquid to a gas.

# HESS'S LAW

## WHAT IS HESS'S LAW?

Some enthalpy changes are easy to measure experimentally, e.g.:
- $\Delta H_c^{\ominus}$, enthalpy change of combustion
- Some values for $\Delta H_f^{\ominus}$, enthalpy change of formation

These can be used to calculate

BECAUSE

Some enthalpy changes that are difficult to measure experimentally, e.g.:
- Some values for $\Delta H_f^{\ominus}$, enthalpy change of formation
- Some values for $\Delta H^{\ominus}$, enthalpy change of reaction

Hess's law states:
**The total enthalpy change for a reaction is the same for any reaction route, provided that the starting and finishing conditions are the same.**

**Hess's law: $\Delta H_1 = \Delta H_2 + \Delta H_3$**

$\Delta H_1$ going this route

A $\xrightarrow{\Delta H_1}$ C

$\Delta H_2$ → B → $\Delta H_3$

is the same as $\Delta H_2 + \Delta H_3$ going this route

## CALCULATING ENTHALPY CHANGES OF FORMATION

**MUST CHECK**

$\Delta H_f^{\ominus}$ and $\Delta H_c^{\ominus}$ definitions on page 52

Step 1: equation for forming **compound** from **elements in standard states**

Step 2: **reactants** and **products** go into an energy cycle

Step 3: **combustion products** go into the energy cycle

Step 4: work out **total enthalpy changes of combustion, $\Delta H_1$ and $\Delta H_2$**

Step 5: use $\Delta H_f^{\ominus} = \Delta H_1 - \Delta H_2$ to calculate $\Delta H_f^{\ominus}$

**Example**
Calculate the standard enthalpy of formation of methane from the following data.

$\Delta H_c^{\ominus}(C) = -393 \text{ kJ mol}^{-1}$
$\Delta H_c^{\ominus}(H_2) = -286 \text{ kJ mol}^{-1}$
$\Delta H_c^{\ominus}(CH_4) = -890 \text{ kJ mol}^{-1}$

$C(s) + 2H_2(g) \rightarrow CH_4(g)$

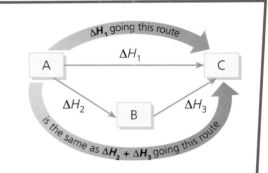

Enthalpy changes of combustion are **easy to measure**.

$\Delta H_f^{\ominus}$

$C(s) + 2H_2(g)$ → $CH_4(g)$

$+ 2O_2(g)$ $\Delta H_1$ $\Delta H_2$ $+ 2O_2(g)$

$CO_2 + 2H_2O(l)$

Both routes need the same amount of $O_2$.

$\Delta H_1 = \Delta H_c^{\ominus}(C) + 2\Delta H_c^{\ominus}(H_2)$

$\Delta H_2 = \Delta H_c^{\ominus}(CH_4)$

$\Delta H_f^{\ominus}(CH_4) = \Delta H_1 - \Delta H_2$

$= -393 + 2(-286) - (-890) \text{ kJ mol}^{-1}$

$= -75 \text{ kJ mol}^{-1}$

2 moles of $H_2$ are in equation.

Take care with + and − signs!

# CALCULATING ENTHALPY CHANGES OF REACTION

Step 1: equation for reaction – sometimes in the question

Step 2: **reactants** and **products** go into an energy cycle

Step 3: **elements** in their **standard states** go into the energy cycle

Step 4: work out **total enthalpy changes of formation**, $\Delta H_1$ and $\Delta H_2$

Step 5: use $\Delta H^\ominus = -\Delta H_1 + \Delta H_2$ to calculate $\Delta H^\ominus$

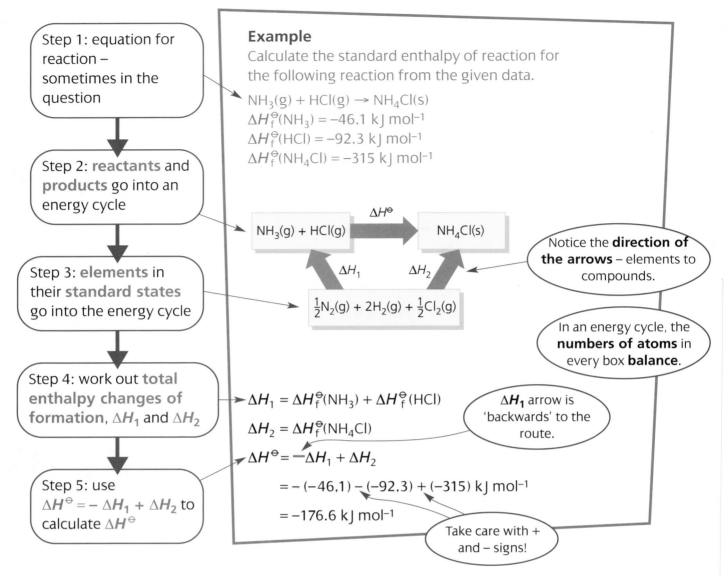

**Example**

Calculate the standard enthalpy of reaction for the following reaction from the given data.

$NH_3(g) + HCl(g) \rightarrow NH_4Cl(s)$

$\Delta H_f^\ominus(NH_3) = -46.1 \text{ kJ mol}^{-1}$

$\Delta H_f^\ominus(HCl) = -92.3 \text{ kJ mol}^{-1}$

$\Delta H_f^\ominus(NH_4Cl) = -315 \text{ kJ mol}^{-1}$

$$NH_3(g) + HCl(g) \xrightarrow{\Delta H^\ominus} NH_4Cl(s)$$

$\Delta H_1$    $\Delta H_2$

$$\tfrac{1}{2}N_2(g) + 2H_2(g) + \tfrac{1}{2}Cl_2(g)$$

Notice the **direction of the arrows** – elements to compounds.

In an energy cycle, the **numbers of atoms** in every box **balance**.

$\Delta H_1 = \Delta H_f^\ominus(NH_3) + \Delta H_f^\ominus(HCl)$

$\Delta H_2 = \Delta H_f^\ominus(NH_4Cl)$

$\Delta H^\ominus = -\Delta H_1 + \Delta H_2$

$\quad = -(-46.1) - (-92.3) + (-315) \text{ kJ mol}^{-1}$

$\quad = -176.6 \text{ kJ mol}^{-1}$

$\Delta H_1$ arrow is 'backwards' to the route.

Take care with + and − signs!

# HESS'S LAW CYCLES

## $\Delta H_f^\ominus$ from $\Delta H_c^\ominus$

Draw the cycle like this:

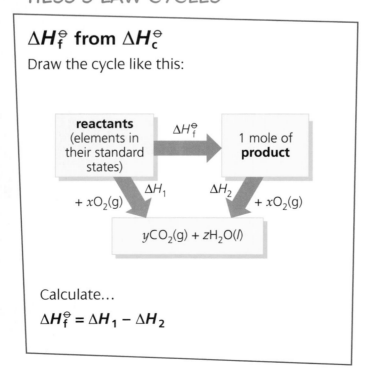

Calculate...

$\Delta H_f^\ominus = \Delta H_1 - \Delta H_2$

## $\Delta H^\ominus$ from $\Delta H_f^\ominus$

Draw the cycle like this:

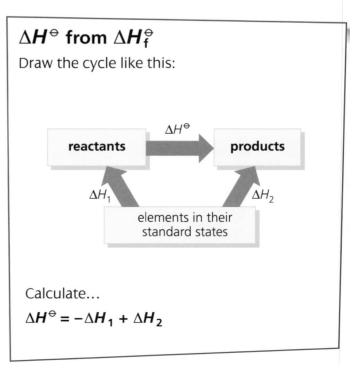

Calculate...

$\Delta H^\ominus = -\Delta H_1 + \Delta H_2$

# MEASURING ENTHALPY CHANGES

## TEMPERATURE CHANGES

- Many reactions take place in aqueous solution – reactants and/or products dissolved in water.
- The **enthalpy change of reaction** causes the temperature of the water to change.

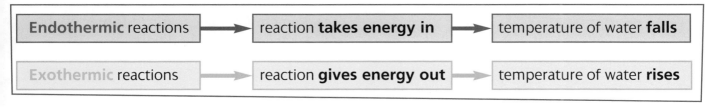

| Endothermic reactions | → | reaction **takes energy in** | → | temperature of water **falls** |
| Exothermic reactions | → | reaction **gives energy out** | → | temperature of water **rises** |

- Enthalpy changes can be calculated from temperature changes using the formula:

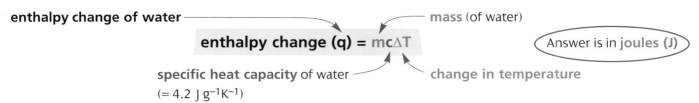

enthalpy change of water ————

mass (of water)

$$\text{enthalpy change (q)} = mc\Delta T$$

Answer is in **joules (J)**

**specific heat capacity** of water ——
$(= 4.2 \, \text{J g}^{-1}\text{K}^{-1})$

change in temperature

## CALCULATING ENTHALPY CHANGE OF NEUTRALISATION, $\Delta H_{neut}$

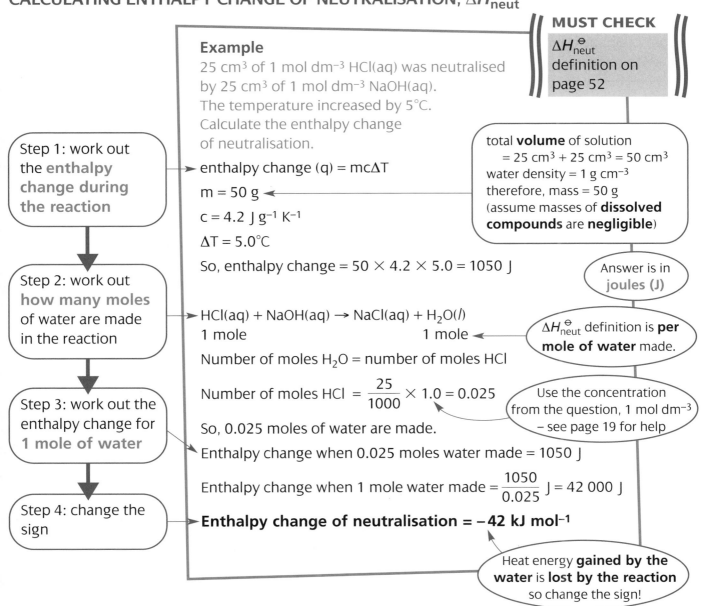

**MUST CHECK**

$\Delta H^{\ominus}_{neut}$ definition on page 52

**Example**
25 cm³ of 1 mol dm⁻³ HCl(aq) was neutralised by 25 cm³ of 1 mol dm⁻³ NaOH(aq).
The temperature increased by 5°C.
Calculate the enthalpy change of neutralisation.

**Step 1: work out the enthalpy change during the reaction**

enthalpy change (q) = mcΔT

m = 50 g

c = 4.2 J g⁻¹ K⁻¹

ΔT = 5.0°C

So, enthalpy change = 50 × 4.2 × 5.0 = 1050 J

total **volume** of solution
= 25 cm³ + 25 cm³ = 50 cm³
water density = 1 g cm⁻³
therefore, mass = 50 g
(assume masses of **dissolved compounds** are **negligible**)

Answer is in joules (J)

**Step 2: work out how many moles of water are made in the reaction**

HCl(aq) + NaOH(aq) → NaCl(aq) + H₂O(l)
1 mole                          1 mole

Number of moles H₂O = number of moles HCl

Number of moles HCl = $\frac{25}{1000}$ × 1.0 = 0.025

So, 0.025 moles of water are made.

$\Delta H^{\ominus}_{neut}$ definition is **per mole of water** made.

Use the concentration from the question, 1 mol dm⁻³ – see page 19 for help

**Step 3: work out the enthalpy change for 1 mole of water**

Enthalpy change when 0.025 moles water made = 1050 J

Enthalpy change when 1 mole water made = $\frac{1050}{0.025}$ J = 42 000 J

**Step 4: change the sign**

**Enthalpy change of neutralisation = −42 kJ mol⁻¹**

Heat energy **gained by the water** is **lost by the reaction** so change the sign!

# COMPARING CALCULATED VALUES WITH DATA BOOK VALUES

**Calculated value** for $\Delta H_{neut}$ is
−42 kJ mol⁻¹
**Data book value** for $\Delta H^{\ominus}_{neut}$ is
−57.2 kJ mol⁻¹

Why the
→
difference?

The measured **temperature change** may not be reliable:
• Heat energy is lost to the surroundings during the experiment, for example, through the walls and top of the container.
• Remember that experiments may not be under **standard conditions**.

## HOW TO IMPROVE THE MEASUREMENT OF TEMPERATURE CHANGE, ΔT

**Step 1:** take temperature readings of alkali every minute.

**Step 3:** stir and take readings from 6th minute onwards.

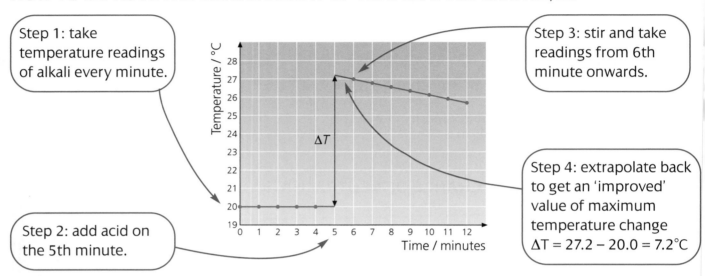

**Step 2:** add acid on the 5th minute.

**Step 4:** extrapolate back to get an 'improved' value of maximum temperature change
ΔT = 27.2 − 20.0 = 7.2°C

Remember: reliability can also be improved by **insulating** the apparatus and using a lid to minimise heat loss!

## CALCULATING ENTHALPY CHANGES OF COMBUSTION, ΔHc

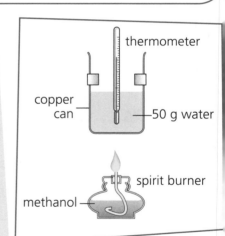
thermometer
copper can
50 g water
methanol
spirit burner

**WORKED EXAMPLE**

0.16 g of methanol was burned in a spirit burner. 50 g of water was heated from 19°C to 23°C.

(a) Calculate the enthalpy change of combustion of methane.

(a) enthalpy change (q) = mcΔT
m = 50 g
c = 4.2 J g⁻¹ K⁻¹
ΔT = 4.0°C
So, enthalpy change of water = 50 × 4.2 × 4.0 = 840 J

Number of moles of methane burned = $\dfrac{mass}{mass\ of\ 1\ mole}$

$= \dfrac{0.16}{16} = 0.01$ moles

When calculating $\Delta H_c$, work out enthalpy change for **1 mole of fuel** burned.

Enthalpy change of water for 1 mole methane = $\dfrac{840}{0.01}$ = 84 000 J = 84 kJ

Enthalpy change of combustion = −84 kJ mol⁻¹

Heat energy **gained by water** is **lost by methane** − CHANGE THE SIGN!!

(b) Comment on why this experimental value is lower than the data book value.

(b) Energy is lost to the surroundings, so that the temperature increase of the water is lower than under ideal conditions.

# COLLISION THEORY

## GRAPHS AND REACTION RATES

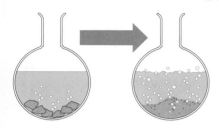

> **Reaction rate** increases – reactions get faster – when:
> - concentration of aqueous solutions increases
> - surface area of solids increases
> - pressure of gases increases.

## REACTION RATE GRAPHS

An easy way of measuring rates is to measure the volume of gas made in a reaction.

The gradient shows how fast the reaction is going:
- horizontal line = no reaction
- shallow gradient = slower reaction
- steep gradient = faster reaction.

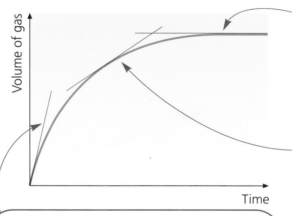

The reaction stops when there is no limiting reagent left.

The rate slows down as the limiting reagent is gradually used up.

Reactions are usually fastest at the start – initial rate of reactioin is greatest.

The **limiting reagent** is the one that gets used up first!

## CHANGING THE RATE

**WORKED EXAMPLE**

Three experiments were carried out to investigate the rate of reaction when excess calcium carbonate reacts with 25 $cm^3$ dilute hydrochloric acid.

$CaCO_3(s) + 2HCl(aq) \rightarrow CaCl_2(aq) + CO_2(g) + H_2O(l)$

Sketch a graph of volume of carbon dioxide produced against time to show how the results from the three reactions are different.

CaCO₃ is in excess. HCl is the **limiting reagent** – it is used up first.

| Experiment | Calcium carbonate | Concentration of acid / mol dm$^{-3}$ |
|---|---|---|
| 1 | large pieces | 1.0 |
| 2 | powdered | 1.0 |
| 3 | large pieces | 0.5 |

1 and 3 – **same surface areas, different concentration of acid**

1 and 2 – **same concentration of acid, different surface areas**

Expt 2: the **amount** of acid not changed – the **same amount** of gas is made.

Expt 2: powdered = **bigger surface area** = **faster** reaction

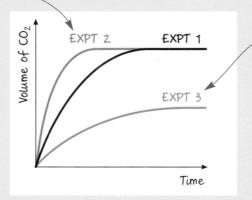

Expt 3: **lower concentration = slower** reaction

Expt 3: lower concentration in same volume = **less acid**

HCl is the limiting reagent so less $CO_2$ is made.

# COLLISION THEORY

**Two key ideas**

For a reaction to happen:
- particles must collide
- with enough energy to react.

Not every collision is successful – if the particles do not have enough energy to react, they will bounce away without a reaction happening.

**MUST CHECK**

Collision theory relating to **energy, temperature and catalysts** on page 65

## INCREASING RATE OF COLLISIONS

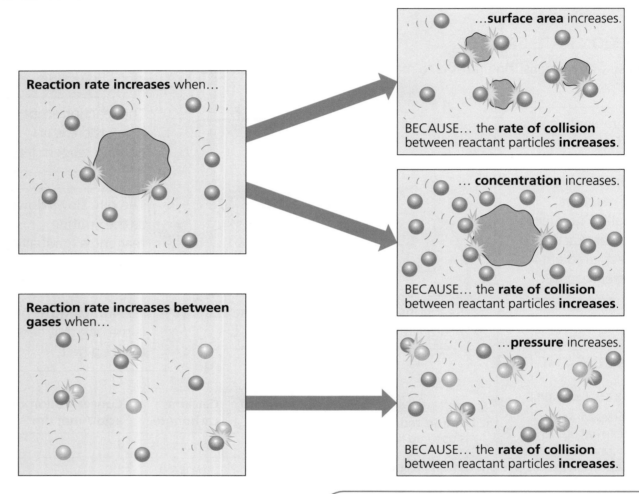

**Reaction rate increases** when…

…**surface area** increases.

BECAUSE… the **rate of collision** between reactant particles **increases**.

… **concentration** increases.

BECAUSE… the **rate of collision** between reactant particles **increases**.

**Reaction rate increases between gases** when…

…**pressure** increases.

BECAUSE… the **rate of collision** between reactant particles **increases**.

This diagram could be of two reactants in solution reacting faster at higher concentrations.

**WORKED EXAMPLE**

Chlorine atoms in the upper atmosphere react with ozone.  $Cl(g) + O_3(g) \rightarrow ClO(g) + O_2(g)$

The concentration of chlorine in the upper atmosphere has increased due to the use of CFCs.
The gas pressure in the upper atmosphere is very low.
Use collision theory to explain how these conditions affect the concentration of ozone.

The **increase in concentration** of chlorine atoms will **increase the rate of reaction**, as there will be **more collisions** between **chlorine atoms and ozone molecules**.
This will lead to a **decrease in the concentration** of ozone.
The **gas pressure is low** therefore gas particles are far apart and there are **very few collisions**. This will lead to a **very slow rate** of reaction. The depletion of ozone is slow.

Always **give the names** of substances where possible – vague, general answers do not always gain as many marks in exams.

# TEMPERATURE

## TEMPERATURE AND REACTION RATES

Fact! Increasing the temperature by 10°C **DOUBLES** the rate of many reactions!

WHY?

**BECAUSE . . .**

Increasing the temperature:

- increases the speed of particles so that their rate of collision increases
- gives the particles more energy – more particles have enough energy to react, so more collisions are successful.

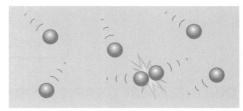

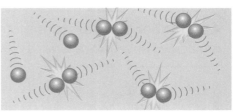

## ENERGY DISTRIBUTION GRAPHS

**Maxwell–Boltzmann distribution curves** show energies of molecules at a particular temperature.

The **area** under the curve represents the **total number of molecules** in the sample.

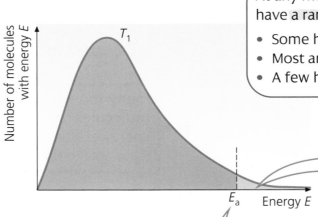

At any moment, different molecules have a range of different energies:

- Some have very low energies.
- Most are in the middle.
- A few have very high energies.

The **proportion of molecules** with enough energy to react is the **area** under this part of the curve.

Molecules with **less energy** than $E_a$ **do not react** when they collide – UNSUCCESSFUL COLLISIONS!

$E_a$ is the **activation energy** – the minimum energy a molecule needs to react.

Molecules with **more energy** than $E_a$ **do react** when they collide – SUCCESSFUL COLLISIONS!

For practice in answering AS Chemistry questions, why not use *Collins Exam Practice AS Chemistry*?

# INCREASING THE TEMPERATURE

**10°C**  **20°C**

When the temperature increases:
- molecules gain more energy
- a greater proportion (i.e. more) molecules have more energy than the activation energy
- more molecules have enough energy to successfully react when they collide.

## DISTRIBUTION GRAPHS FOR DIFFERENT TEMPERATURES

**At a higher temperature** more molecules have **more energy**.

The curve is flatter because…
the number of molecules = the **area** under the curve … so the **total area** must **stay the same**.

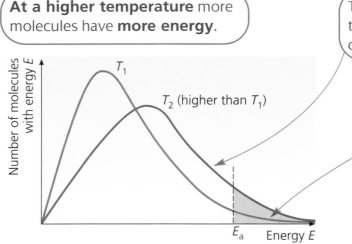

**IMPORTANT!**
The **proportion of molecules** that have **more energy** than the activation energy **increases**.

**THEREFORE**

There are many more successful collisions → reaction rate increases

| Even a **small** temperature rise | causes | a **large increase** in the **area** **under the** **curve** above $E_a$ | therefore | **many more** **molecules** have energy of at least $E_a$ so able to react | therefore | **much faster** reaction. | **!** |

---

**WORKED EXAMPLE**

The diagram shows a distribution curve of molecular energies of chlorine atoms and ozone molecules at a temperature $T_1$.

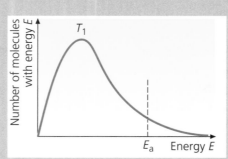

$E_a$ is the activation energy for the reaction
$Cl(g) + O_3(g) \rightarrow ClO(g) + O_2(g)$

(a) Shade the diagram to show the proportion of molecules that have sufficient energy to react on collision.
(b) $T_1$ is the winter temperature of the ozone layer over Antarctica. $T_2$ is the higher, summer temperature. Sketch a curve on the graph to show the distribution of molecular energies at the higher temperature, $T_2$. Explain how raising the temperature affects the rate of reaction.

a)

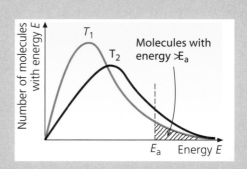

(b) The rise in temperature causes a **large increase in the rate of reaction**, because a **much greater proportion** of **Cl atoms and $O_3$ molecules** have more energy than the **activation energy**, resulting in a large increase in the **rate of successful collisions**.

# CATALYSTS

## WHAT IS A CATALYST?

Rate is usually **faster**.

Catalysts change **rate** but **do not affect** the **amount** of product – the **position of equilibrium** is not affected.

A **catalyst** changes the rate of a reaction without being permanently changed.

Catalysts take part in reactions but are **regenerated** at the end.

## CATALYSTS AND ACTIVATION ENERGY

**Catalysts lower the activation energy.**

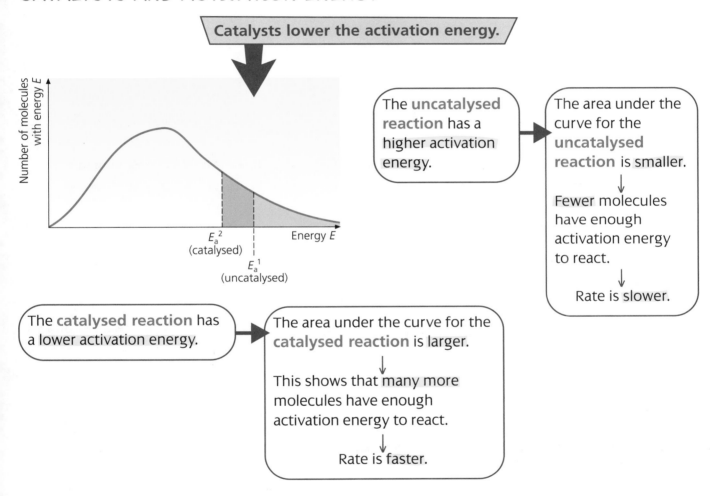

The **uncatalysed reaction** has a higher activation energy.

The area under the curve for the **uncatalysed reaction** is smaller.

↓

Fewer molecules have enough activation energy to react.

↓

Rate is slower.

The **catalysed reaction** has a lower activation energy.

The area under the curve for the **catalysed reaction** is larger.

↓

This shows that many more molecules have enough activation energy to react.

↓

Rate is faster.

## COSTS OF CATALYSTS IN INDUSTRY

£

- Catalysts have a high purchase cost.
- They are regenerated so can be re-used.
- Using a catalyst requires much less energy than using a higher temperature.

BUT ...

- Over time, catalysts can become 'poisoned' by dirt/impurities/contaminants.
- Catalysts must eventually be cleaned or replaced.

# CATALYSTS AND ENTHALPY PROFILE DIAGRAMS

Catalysts provide a different reaction pathway with a lower activation energy.

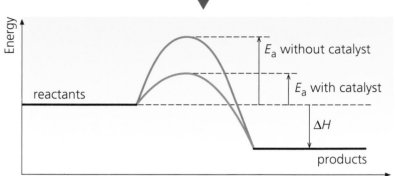

The catalyst provides a **different pathway** for the reaction.

The value of $E_a$ is **lower** when a catalyst is used.

Notice that the value of $\Delta H$ is **not changed**.

---

**WORKED EXAMPLE**

(a) Use Maxwell–Boltzmann distribution and enthalpy profile diagrams to explain why using catalysts increases reaction rate.

(b) Suggest reasons why using catalysts leads to lower running costs than using a high temperature to increase the rate of industrial processes.

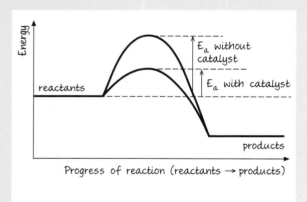

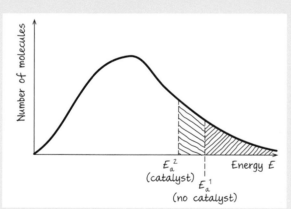

(a) A catalyst **lowers the activation energy** by providing a **different pathway for the reaction**. This means that **more molecules** have **the minimum energy** (**activation energy**) to react. Therefore the **rate of the reaction increases**.

(b) Both increasing temperature and using a catalyst increase rate, however, running costs increase at higher temperatures due to **fuel costs**. Catalysts are not used up – they are **regenerated**, so the **running costs** of using a catalyst are **lower**.

# CATALYSTS IN ACTION

## OZONE DEPLETION

start
OCR only

- Ozone in the ozone layer breaks down naturally by absorbing UV light – this stops harmful UV from reaching Earth.
- Chlorine atoms act as **catalysts** in speeding up the destruction of ozone.
- Cl atoms come from the breakdown of CFCs – chlorofluorocarbons.

> Cl is a **homogeneous** catalyst – it is in the same state as ozone (i.e. both are gases).

> Cl forms an intermediate – ClO

$$Cl(g) + O_3(g) \rightarrow ClO(g) + O_2(g)$$

$$ClO(g) + O(g) \rightarrow Cl(g) + O_2(g)$$

> Cl is regenerated – therefore it is not used up.

Overall change

$$\cancel{Cl(g)} + O_3(g) + \cancel{ClO(g)} + O(g) \rightarrow \cancel{ClO(g)} + O_2(g) + \cancel{Cl(g)} + O_2(g)$$

> The overall equation does not show Cl. It is a catalyst.

$$O_3(g) + O(g) \rightarrow O_2(g) + O_2(g)$$

> The ozone is broken down **faster** and without absorbing UV light.

> The reaction follows a different pathway with a lower activation energy.

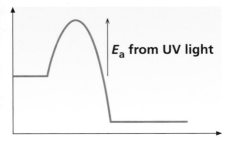

$E_a$ **from UV light**

Uncatalysed reaction

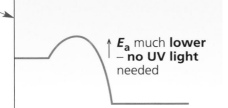

$E_a$ much **lower – no UV light** needed

Catalysed reaction

## HOMOGENEOUS AND HETEROGENEOUS CATALYSTS

> **Homogeneous** catalysts:
> - are in the same state as the reactants that they catalyse
> - often work by forming intermediates.

Examples of homogeneous catalysts:
- chlorine atoms reacting with ozone
- $H^+(aq)$ catalysts in esterification reactions – see page 130

**Homogeneous** catalysts = same state

**Heterogeneous** catalysts = different states

**Heterogeneous** catalysts:
- are usually solids catalysing reactions in different states – e.g. gases/aqueous solutions
- work by forming temporary bonds with reactants on the solid surface
- ensure that reactant molecules are brought together so that they can react, and then leave as product molecules.

Examples of heterogeneous catalysts:
- Fe in the Haber process – see page 77
- oil processing catalysts – see page 101
- nickel in making margarine – see page 110
- catalysts in catalytic converters

end
OCR only

**68**

# CATALYTIC CONVERTERS

start
OCR and AQA only

Catalytic converters:
- **decrease emissions** of carbon monoxide (CO) and nitrogen oxide ($NO_x$) from car exhausts
- contain **heterogeneous** catalysts – **solids** that catalyse reactions in gases
- catalyse redox reactions between the exhaust gases.

**MUST CHECK**
- Redox reactions on pages 43 and 45
- Pollutants from fuels on page 100

---

**ADSORPTION**
Gas molecules form **weak bonds** with the solid catalyst

**REACTION**
The molecules **react** together to form different products

**DESORPTION**
The **weak bonds break** and new products **leave** the catalyst surface

Pollutant gases from the engine:
- CO
- $NO_x$
- unburnt hydrocarbons

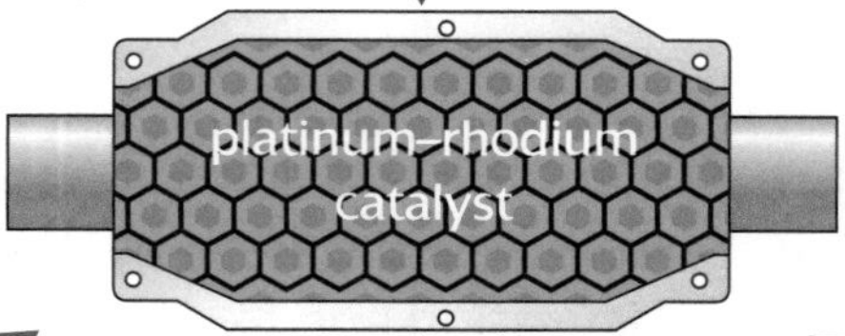

platinum–rhodium catalyst

Less harmful gases to the air:
- $CO_2$
- $N_2$
- $H_2O$

The catalyst is powdered on a mesh to increase the surface area.

Several reactions happen in the converter. For example:
$2NO(g) + 2CO(g) \rightarrow N_2(g) + 2CO_2(g)$

The catalyst only works when hot – above 150°C.

- This reaction does not happen at this temperature without a catalyst.
- The catalyst provides a different pathway (**adsorption → reaction → desorption**) with a lower activation energy.

**WORKED EXAMPLE**

The following reaction happens in a catalytic converter.

$2NO(g) + 2CO(g) \rightarrow N_2(g) + 2CO_2(g)$

(a) Show, by using oxidation states, that this reaction is a redox reaction.

(b) Outline how the rate of this reaction is increased in the converter.

(c) Explain, with reference to activation energy, why the converter does not work when cold.

(a) Oxidation states

$2NO(g) + 2CO(g) \rightarrow N_2(g) + 2CO_2(g)$

[Ox]  +2 –2    +2 –2        0      +4 –2

This is a redox reaction because **N is reduced** from oxidation state **+2 to 0**.
C is oxidised from oxidation state +2 to +4.

(b) The reaction rate is **increased** by:
- the use of a **catalyst** (platinum–rhodium alloy)
- the **surface area** of the catalyst is **very large** (powder on mesh)
- the converter runs at a **high temperature**.

(c) At low temperatures the molecules do not have the minimum energy (activation energy) necessary to react.

end
OCR and AQA only

# DYNAMIC EQUILIBRIUM

## WHAT IS EQUILIBRIUM?

- **Reversible** reactions reach **equilibrium**.
- This is a state of balance where the concentrations (for aqueous solutions) and pressures (for gases) of reactants and products remain constant.

**MUST REMEMBER**
- Always talk about **'concentrations'** rather than **'amounts'**.

## CARBON DIOXIDE IN SPARKLING WATER

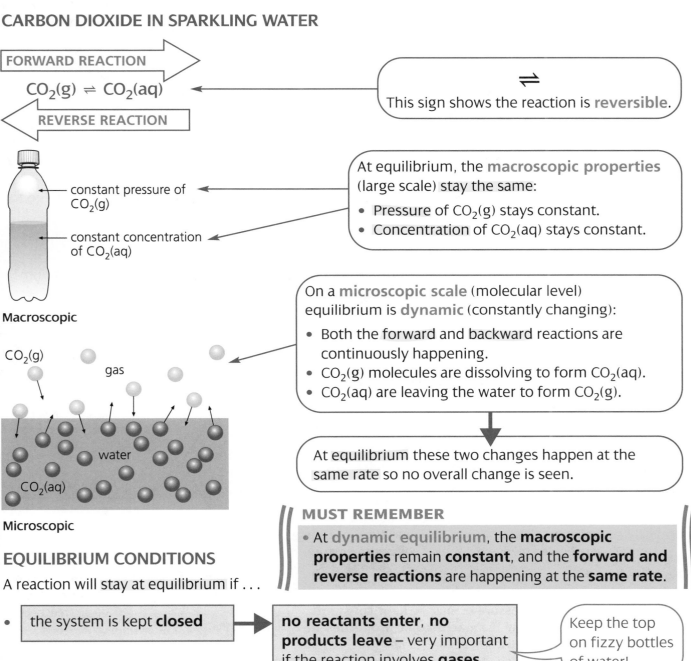

**FORWARD REACTION**

$$CO_2(g) \rightleftharpoons CO_2(aq)$$

**REVERSE REACTION**

$\rightleftharpoons$
This sign shows the reaction is **reversible**.

constant pressure of $CO_2(g)$

constant concentration of $CO_2(aq)$

At equilibrium, the **macroscopic properties** (large scale) stay the same:
- Pressure of $CO_2(g)$ stays constant.
- Concentration of $CO_2(aq)$ stays constant.

**Macroscopic**

$CO_2(g)$     gas

water

$CO_2(aq)$

**Microscopic**

On a **microscopic scale** (molecular level) equilibrium is **dynamic** (constantly changing):
- Both the forward and backward reactions are continuously happening.
- $CO_2(g)$ molecules are dissolving to form $CO_2(aq)$.
- $CO_2(aq)$ are leaving the water to form $CO_2(g)$.

At equilibrium these two changes happen at the same rate so no overall change is seen.

**MUST REMEMBER**
- At **dynamic equilibrium**, the **macroscopic properties** remain **constant**, and the **forward and reverse reactions** are happening at the **same rate**.

## EQUILIBRIUM CONDITIONS

A reaction will stay at equilibrium if . . .

- the system is kept **closed** → **no reactants enter**, **no products leave** – very important if the reaction involves **gases**

  Keep the top on fizzy bottles of water!

  **AND**

- **temperature** stays constant → see page 73

  Warm fizzy water loses its fizz!

  **AND**

- **pressure** stays constant → see page 72

  Fizzy water is made by dissolving carbon dioxide under pressure.

# CONCENTRATION AND EQUILIBRIUM

Hydrogen gas reacts with iodine vapour to form hydrogen iodide gas:

$$H_2(g) + I_2(g) \rightleftharpoons 2HI(g)$$

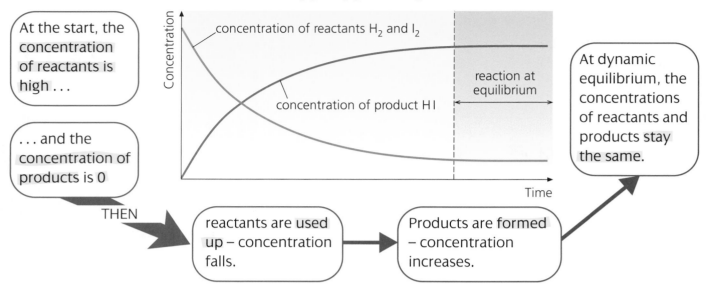

> At the start, the concentration of reactants is high . . .

> . . . and the concentration of products is 0

THEN

> reactants are used up – concentration falls.

> Products are formed – concentration increases.

> At dynamic equilibrium, the concentrations of reactants and products stay the same.

## KEY POINTS

- The reactants are never completely used up – the reaction reaches equilibrium, it does not 'go to completion' – there are always some reactants and some products present.
- This is a reaction between gases – it is very important that the system stays closed, so no gases escape, and the pressure stays constant.
- For gaseous reactions, either the concentration or the pressure can be measured at equilibrium.
- Equilibrium can be reached from either side of the equation – it is reversible. So if pure HI(g) were used, it would decompose to form $H_2(g)$ and $I_2(g)$, and the same equilibrium would be reached.

### WORKED EXAMPLE

If a mixture of $NO_2$ and CO is heated, the following reaction reaches equilibrium.

$$NO_2(g) + CO(g) \rightleftharpoons NO(g) + CO_2(g)$$

The graph alongside shows the concentration changes in a mixture of $NO_2$ and CO.

(a) What conditions need to be kept constant to make these measurements?

(b) Use this reaction to discuss the differences between macroscopic and microscopic properties of dynamic equilibrium.

(c) Sketch a similar graph to show how the concentration changes if NO and $CO_2$ were heated to give the same equilibrium mixture.

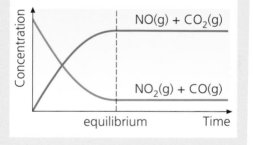

(a) The reactants and products are all gases. The system must be **closed,** ✔ and the **temperature** ✔ and **pressure** ✔ must be **kept constant**.

> 3 key points ✔✔✔

(b) At **dynamic equilibrium**, the **macroscopic properties** are **constant** ✔ i.e. **concentrations** of reactants ($NO_2$ + CO) and products (NO and $CO_2$) stay constant ✔. However, at a **microscopic level** the equilibrium is **dynamic** ✔ because both the forward and backward reactions are happening ✔. As these reactions happen at the **same rate** ✔, no overall change is seen ✔.

> Concentrations of **reactants NO and $CO_2$ start high**.

> The **same equilibrium concentrations** are reached.

(c)

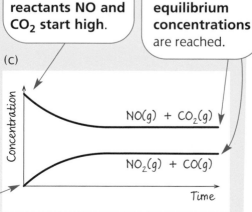

### MUST REMEMBER

- to discuss both macro and micro!
- to give the names or formulae of the reactants and products in the question!

> Concentrations of **products $NO_2$ and CO start at 0**.

# LE CHATELIER'S PRINCIPLE

## LE CHATELIER'S PRINCIPLE

Conditions, for example:
- **concentration**
- **pressure** – page 72
- **temperature** – page 73

System must be **closed** (sealed) – especially important for **gases**.

If a **change in conditions** is made to a **closed system** in equilibrium, the system responds to **counteract the change** as much as possible.

The **direction** of the reaction moves **against** the change.

But what about catalysts ?

**Catalysts** do not affect the position of equilibrium! They only speed up the rate of reaching equilibrium – get there faster!

## CHANGING THE CONCENTRATION

**TWO GENERAL RULES!**

1. If the concentration of a substance is increased, the system will counteract the change by forcing the reaction to go in the direction that uses up the 'extra' substance.

2. If the concentration of a substance is decreased, the system will counteract the change by forcing the reaction to go in the direction that makes more of the substance.

### FOUR POSSIBLE CHANGES . . .

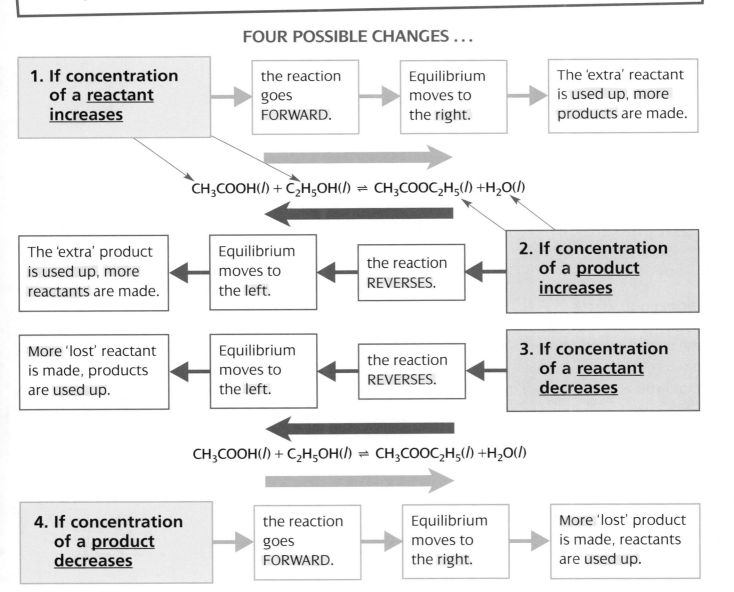

**1. If concentration of a reactant increases** → the reaction goes FORWARD. → Equilibrium moves to the right. → The 'extra' reactant is used up, more products are made.

$$CH_3COOH(l) + C_2H_5OH(l) \rightleftharpoons CH_3COOC_2H_5(l) + H_2O(l)$$

The 'extra' product is used up, more reactants are made. ← Equilibrium moves to the left. ← the reaction REVERSES. ← **2. If concentration of a product increases**

More 'lost' reactant is made, products are used up. ← Equilibrium moves to the left. ← the reaction REVERSES. ← **3. If concentration of a reactant decreases**

$$CH_3COOH(l) + C_2H_5OH(l) \rightleftharpoons CH_3COOC_2H_5(l) + H_2O(l)$$

**4. If concentration of a product decreases** → the reaction goes FORWARD. → Equilibrium moves to the right. → More 'lost' product is made, reactants are used up.

# CHANGING THE PRESSURE

- Changing the pressure affects **all the substances in the equation**.
- The system will change to **counteract the total pressure change**.

## TWO GENERAL RULES

1. Increasing the pressure moves the equilibrium to the side of the equation with **fewer gas molecules**.

2. Decreasing the pressure moves the equilibrium to the side of the equation with **more gas molecules**.

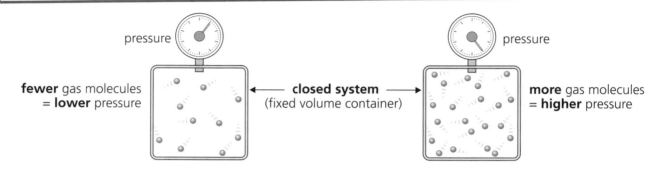

**fewer** gas molecules = **lower** pressure

**closed system** (fixed volume container)

**more** gas molecules = **higher** pressure

### TWO POSSIBLE CHANGES ...

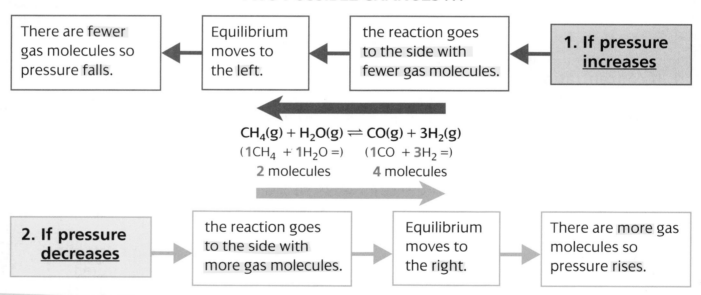

| There are **fewer** gas molecules so pressure falls. | ← | Equilibrium moves to the left. | ← | the reaction goes to the side with **fewer gas molecules**. | ← | **1. If pressure increases** |

$$CH_4(g) + H_2O(g) \rightleftharpoons CO(g) + 3H_2(g)$$
(1CH$_4$ + 1H$_2$O =)   (1CO + 3H$_2$ =)
2 molecules        4 molecules

| **2. If pressure decreases** | → | the reaction goes to the side with **more gas molecules**. | → | Equilibrium moves to the right. | → | There are **more gas** molecules so pressure rises. |

## WORKED EXAMPLE

Ethanol is made on an industrial scale by reacting ethene with steam at 300°C.

$$C_2H_4(g) + H_2O(g) \rightleftharpoons C_2H_5OH(g)$$

Explain the effect that each of the following changes has on the yield of ethanol.

(a) Increasing the pressure
(b) Increasing the concentration of ethene
(c) Using a catalyst

(a) Increasing the pressure would **increase** the yield of ethanol.
There are two molecules on the left of the equation and only one on the right. The system would act to **reduce the increased pressure** by forming **fewer gas molecules**, moving the equilibrium to the right (**forward** reaction).

(b) Increasing the concentration of ethene would **increase** the yield of ethanol. The system would act to **reduce the increased concentration** by moving to the right (**forward** reaction) and forming **more products**.

(c) Catalysts have no effect on yield – they only affect the rate.

# TEMPERATURE CHANGES AND EQUILIBRIUM

## LE CHATELIER

**Le Chatelier's principle** also works for temperature changes.

If the temperature is changed, the system will counteract the change as much as possible:

- If the **temperature is increased**, the reaction will go in the direction that **reduces** the temperature by **taking in energy** (i.e. the **endothermic** direction).
- If the temperature is decreased, the reaction will go in the direction that increases the temperature by giving out energy (i.e. the exothermic direction).

### EXOTHERMIC CHANGES

$$N_2(g) + 3H_2(g) \rightleftharpoons 2NH_3(g) \quad \Delta H^\ominus = -92 \text{ kJ mol}^{-1}$$

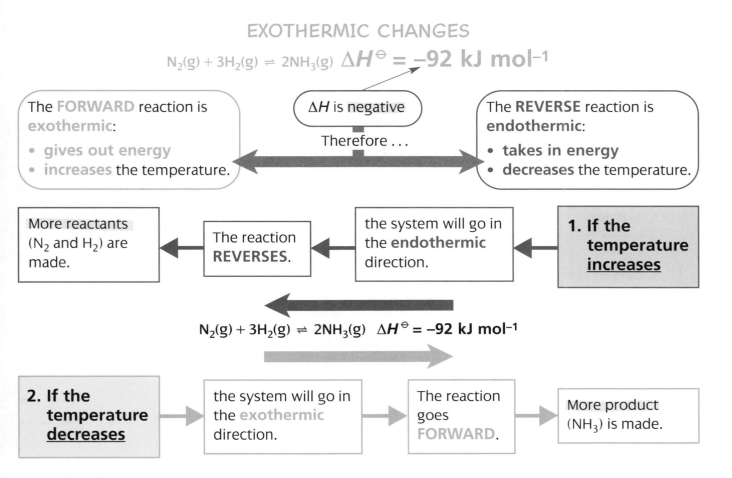

The **FORWARD** reaction is exothermic:
- gives out energy
- increases the temperature.

$\Delta H$ is negative

Therefore ...

The **REVERSE** reaction is endothermic:
- **takes in energy**
- **decreases** the temperature.

More reactants ($N_2$ and $H_2$) are made. ← The reaction **REVERSES**. ← the system will go in the **endothermic** direction. ← **1. If the temperature increases**

$$N_2(g) + 3H_2(g) \rightleftharpoons 2NH_3(g) \quad \Delta H^\ominus = -92 \text{ kJ mol}^{-1}$$

**2. If the temperature decreases** → the system will go in the exothermic direction. → The reaction goes **FORWARD**. → More product ($NH_3$) is made.

---

**MUST REMEMBER**

**Increased temperature** causes **endothermic** reaction.

**Decreased temperature** causes exothermic reaction.

**YIELD AND RATE**

For exothermic reactions, the maximum yield (the most products) is made at low temperatures.

**BUT ...**

The rate is too slow at low temperatures

**SO ...**

A 'compromise' is often reached to get a reasonable yield at a fast rate.

**MUST CHECK**

'The Haber process' (page 77) and 'Manufacture of sulphuric acid' (page 79)

# ENDOTHERMIC CHANGES

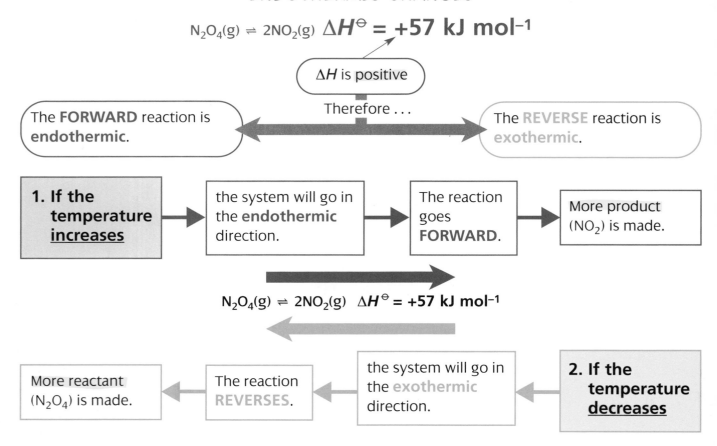

$$N_2O_4(g) \rightleftharpoons 2NO_2(g) \quad \Delta H^\ominus = +57 \text{ kJ mol}^{-1}$$

$\Delta H$ is positive

Therefore . . .

The **FORWARD** reaction is **endothermic**.

The **REVERSE** reaction is **exothermic**.

**1. If the temperature <u>increases</u>** → the system will go in the **endothermic** direction. → The reaction goes **FORWARD**. → More product ($NO_2$) is made.

$$N_2O_4(g) \rightleftharpoons 2NO_2(g) \quad \Delta H^\ominus = +57 \text{ kJ mol}^{-1}$$

More reactant ($N_2O_4$) is made. ← The reaction **REVERSES**. ← the system will go in the **exothermic** direction. ← **2. If the temperature <u>decreases</u>**

## CHOOSING THE CONDITIONS

- For industrial processes, the best conditions give high yields (more products) at a fast rate.
- Changing conditions affects both rate and position of equilibrium.
- 'Compromise conditions' of pressure and temperature are used to give reasonable yields at fast rates.

| Change in conditions | Effect on rate | Effect on position of equilibrium |
|---|---|---|
| **Increased concentration** of reactants | **Faster** | Moves to the right<br>More products = **higher yield** |
| **Increased pressure** (gases) | **Faster** | Moves to the side of the reaction with **fewer gas molecules**<br>For some reactions this decreases yield |
| **Increased temperature** | **Faster** | Moves in the **endothermic** direction<br>For exothermic reactions this **decreases** yield |
| Use of a **catalyst** | **Faster** | **No effect** |

**WORKED EXAMPLE**

Explain whether the yield of the following reactions would increase or decrease if the temperature was increased.

(a) $C_2H_4(g) + H_2O(g) \rightleftharpoons C_2H_5OH(g)$      $\Delta H = -46 \text{ kJ mol}^{-1}$
(b) $N_2(g) + O_2(g) \rightleftharpoons 2NO(g)$      $\Delta H = +90 \text{ kJ mol}^{-1}$
(c) $H_2O(g) + C(s) \rightleftharpoons CO(g) + H_2(g)$      $\Delta H = +13 \text{ kJ mol}^{-1}$

(a) The reaction is **exothermic** in the forward direction. An increase in the temperature moves the reaction in the **endothermic** direction, so it **reverses** and **less yield** of $C_2H_5OH$ is formed.
(b) The reaction is **endothermic** in the forward direction. An increase in the temperature moves the reaction in the **endothermic** direction, so it **goes forward** and **more yield** of NO is formed.
(c) The reaction is **endothermic** in the forward direction. An increase in the temperature moves the reaction in the **endothermic** direction, so it **goes forward** and **more yield** of CO and $H_2$ is formed.

# PROPERTIES OF ACIDS

## REACTIONS OF DILUTE ACIDS

start
OCR and Edexcel only

### **4** reactions to remember!

**1. metal + acid → salt + hydrogen**
e.g.
$Mg(s) + 2HCl(aq) → MgCl_2(aq) + H_2(g)$

**2. metal oxide + acid → salt + water**
e.g.
$MgO(s) + 2HCl(aq) → MgCl_2(aq) + H_2O(l)$

Which salt?
- **Hydrochloric acid** gives a **metal chloride**.
- **Sulphuric acid** gives a **metal sulphate**.
- **Nitric acid** gives a **metal nitrate**.

Metals oxides are **basic**. Bases **neutralise** acids.

**Water** is usually formed when acids react.

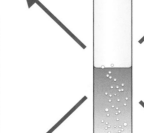

**3. metal carbonate + acid → salt + water + carbon dioxide**
e.g.
$MgCO_3(s) + 2HCl(aq) → MgCl_2(aq) + H_2O(l) + CO_2(g)$

**4. metal hydroxide + acid → salt + water**
e.g.
$NaOH(aq) + HCl(aq) → NaCl(aq) + H_2O(l)$

**Alkalis** are **soluble bases**. This is an important reaction – it is used in **titrations** to measure acid concentration (see page 20).

## IONIC EQUATION FOR NEUTRALISATION

- All dilute acids contain **H⁺ ions** in aqueous solution.
- Acids usually form water when they are neutralised.
- The ionic equation for neutralisation is the same for all dilute acids:

$$H^+(aq) + OH^-(aq) → H_2O(l)$$

hydrochloric acid (HCl)
ions: $H^+(aq) + Cl^-(aq)$

sulphuric acid ($H_2SO_4$)
ions: $2H^+(aq) + SO_4^{2-}(aq)$

nitric acid ($HNO_3$)
ions: $H^+(aq) + NO_3^-(aq)$

All acids give up **H⁺** when they react.

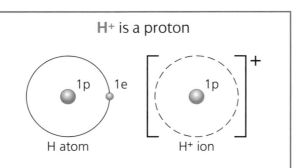

$H^+$ is a proton

1p  1e

1p

+

H atom

H⁺ ion

**MUST REMEMBER**
- An acid is a **proton donor**.

end
OCR and Edexcel only

# STRONG AND WEAK ACIDS

start
OCR only

Hydrochloric acid is a **strong acid**:

$$HCl(g) \rightarrow H^+(aq) + Cl^-(aq)$$

Ethanoic acid is a **weak acid**:

$$CH_3COOH(aq) \rightleftharpoons H^+(aq) + CH_3COO^-(aq)$$

The arrow shows that all the HCl molecules are **completely dissociated** to form **H⁺** ions.

The **reversible** sign shows that the reaction goes **both ways** and an **equilibrium** is reached. Only a **small percentage** of $CH_3COOH$ molecules **dissociate** to form **H⁺** ions.

**H⁺(aq)**

## MUST REMEMBER

- **A strong acid completely dissociates** into ions when it dissolves in water.
- **A weak acid partially dissociates** into ions when it dissolves in water.

## COMPARING STRONG AND WEAK ACIDS

### MUST TAKE CARE

- Must not muddle up **strength** and **concentration**:
  - A **single type of acid** can be diluted to give **different concentrations**.
  - **Different types** of acids have **different strengths** – to compare them fairly, use the **same concentration** e.g. 1 mol dm⁻³ HCl(aq) and 1 mol dm⁻³ $CH_3COOH$(aq).

At the same concentration . . .

| A strong acid | A weak acid |
|---|---|
| • is completely dissociated into **H⁺** ions | • is partially dissociated into **H⁺** ions |
| • has a higher electrical conductivity | • has a lower electrical conductivity |
| • has a very low pH (1 or 2) | • has a higher pH (3 to 6) |
| • is very corrosive | • is less corrosive |
| • reacts more quickly | • reacts more slowly |

Food acids such as citric acid are weak acids.

## WORKED EXAMPLE

(a) In an experiment, magnesium hydroxide reacted with hydrochloric acid (a strong acid). Write an equation for the reaction.
(b) The experiment was repeated using magnesium hydroxide with a weak acid of the same concentration. Give the similarities and differences between the two reactions.
(c) Suggest a simple test to distinguish between a strong and a weak acid of the same concentration.

(a) $Mg(OH)_2(s) + 2HCl(aq) \rightarrow MgCl_2(aq) + 2H_2O(l)$

First work out the **formula** of $Mg(OH)_2$, then **balance** it – see pages 22 and 13.

(b)

| Similarities | Differences |
|---|---|
| • both are neutralisation reactions | • reaction with hydrochloric acid is faster |
| • both form water as a product | • salt formed by the weak acid is not magnesium chloride |
| • the ionic equation for both reactions is the same | |

(c) Test pH using Universal Indicator or a pH probe. The strong acid has a lower pH.

end
OCR only

# THE HABER PROCESS

start
OCR and
Edexcel only

## INDUSTRIAL MANUFACTURE OF AMMONIA

**MUST CHECK**

Le Chatelier's principle on pages 71 and 73

Industrial processes . . .
. . . make as much product as possible, as fast as possible!

This is a **reversible** reaction that reaches **equilibrium**. To get a **high yield**, conditions must be chosen to shift equilibrium to the **right**.

ammonia

$$N_2(g) + 3H_2(g) \rightleftharpoons 2NH_3(g) \quad \Delta H = -92 \text{ kJ mol}^{-1}$$

**MUST REMEMBER**
- **Higher temperatures and pressures** make reactions **faster**!

$(1N_2 + 3H_2 =)$
4 gas molecules

2 gas molecules

The reaction is **exothermic**.
A **higher temperature** will shift equilibrium to the **left** (**endothermic** direction).

A **higher pressure** will shift equilibrium to the **right** (**fewer** gas molecules).

## CHOOSING THE CONDITIONS

Look at the line for any pressure:
- as **temperature increases**, the **yield decreases**.

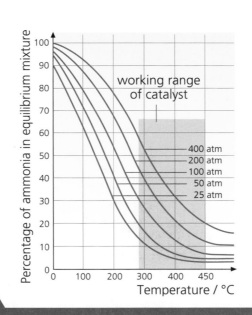

working range of catalyst

400 atm
200 atm
100 atm
50 atm
25 atm

Percentage of ammonia in equilibrium mixture

Temperature / °C

Look at the different pressures:
- as **pressure increases**, the **yield increases**.

Conditions for the highest yield:
- high pressure
- low temperature

Therefore . . .

Conditions for the highest rate:
- high pressure
- high temperature

High pressure increases **yield** <u>and</u> **rate**.

**VERY high pressures** (e.g. 400 atm) are **too expensive and unsafe** to operate on a large scale.

**COMPROMISE!**
The conditions used in industry are:
- 200 atm pressure
- 450°C temperature
- finely divided iron catalyst.

- Very low temperatures give high yield but are too slow.
- 450°C is a **'compomise'** – a **moderate yield** at a **fast rate**.
- Unreacted $N_2$ and $H_2$ are **recycled** back into the process so are finally almost completely converted into $NH_3$.

Using a **catalyst speeds up** the reaction but has **no effect on the final yield**.

# WHY THE HABER PROCESS IS IMPORTANT

- The element nitrogen is an unreactive gas – 78% of the atmosphere is nitrogen.
- Compounds of nitrogen are used daily on an enormous scale.
- The **Haber process** converts atmospheric nitrogen into a nitrogen compound (ammonia) – the starting compound for a very wide range of other nitrogen compounds.

Uses of nitrogen compounds:
- fertilisers
- explosives – e.g. TNT
- polyamides – e.g. nylon

## PRODUCTS FROM AMMONIA

Ammonia is a **base**. It neutralises acids to form **salts**.
For example:

    **sulphuric acid**    **ammonium sulphate**

$2NH_3 + H_2SO_4 \rightarrow (NH_4)_2SO_4$

    **nitric acid**    **ammonium nitrate**

$NH_3 + HNO_3 \rightarrow NH_4NO_3$

All ammonium salts contain the **ammonium ion**:
$$NH_4^+$$

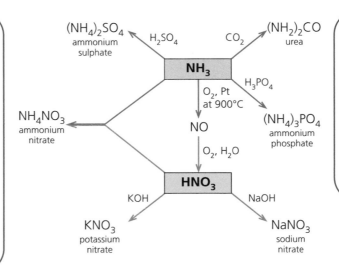

$(NH_4)_2SO_4$ ammonium sulphate

$H_2SO_4$

$CO_2$

$(NH_2)_2CO$ urea

**NH₃**

$H_3PO_4$

$O_2$, Pt at 900°C

$(NH_4)_3PO_4$ ammonium phosphate

$NH_4NO_3$ ammonium nitrate

NO

$O_2$, $H_2O$

**HNO₃**

KOH

NaOH

$KNO_3$ potassium nitrate

$NaNO_3$ sodium nitrate

Ammonia can be converted to **nitric acid**.
This reacts with alkalis to form **nitrate** salts.
All nitrates contain the **nitrate ion**:
$$NO_3^-$$

Ammonium salts are used in fertilisers.

Nitrates are used as fertilisers and to make explosives.

---

**WORKED EXAMPLE**

The first stage in the manufacture of nitric acid involves the oxidation of ammonia.

$4NH_3(g) + 5O_2(g) \rightleftharpoons 4NO(g) + 6H_2O(g)$    $\Delta H = -909$ kJ mol⁻¹

The conditions used for the reaction are:

- 900°C
- 10 atm pressure
- platinum–rhodium catalyst.

Discuss, in terms of equilibium and rate, why these conditions are chosen.

Make sure the key words in the question, 'equilibrium' and 'rate', are used in the answer.

Temperature: The reaction is **exothermic** ($\Delta H$ is negative) so a **high temperature** will drive equilibrium to the **left** (the **endothermic direction**) **leading to a reduced yield**. However, a **low temperature** will lead to a very **slow** rate. At 900°C, the rate will be **fast** with a **low yield**. However, the unreacted gases can be recycled to improve the percentage conversion of reactants to products.

Pressure: Reactants: **9** gas molecules. Products: **10** gas molecules.
Yield will be **higher** at **low pressures**, as equilibrium will move to the **right**. However, rate is **very slow** at low pressures. 10 atm pressure is a **'compromise'** between a faster rate and a moderate yield.

In 'long answers' make sure that **every condition** is discussed!

Catalyst: The catalyst will **increase** the rate but has no effect on the position of equilibrium – the yield.

end

OCR and Edexcel only

# THE CONTACT PROCESS

start
Edexcel only

## MANUFACTURE OF SULPHURIC ACID

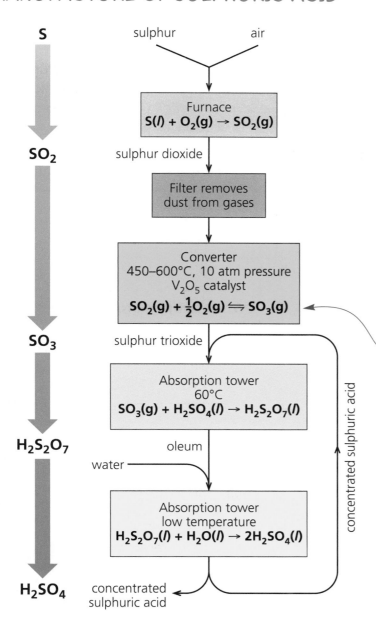

**S**

**SO$_2$**

**SO$_3$**

**H$_2$S$_2$O$_7$**

**H$_2$SO$_4$**

sulphur          air

Furnace
**S($l$) + O$_2$(g) → SO$_2$(g)**

sulphur dioxide

Filter removes
dust from gases

Converter
450–600°C, 10 atm pressure
V$_2$O$_5$ catalyst
**SO$_2$(g) + $\frac{1}{2}$O$_2$(g) ⇌ SO$_3$(g)**

sulphur trioxide

Absorption tower
60°C
**SO$_3$(g) + H$_2$SO$_4$($l$) → H$_2$S$_2$O$_7$($l$)**

oleum

water

Absorption tower
low temperature
**H$_2$S$_2$O$_7$($l$) + H$_2$O($l$) → 2H$_2$SO$_4$($l$)**

concentrated
sulphuric acid

concentrated sulphuric acid

**Flow charts** show industrial processes:
- The arrows show the 'flow' of reactants and products in and out.
- The boxes often show the processes happening in different parts of the chemical plant – reaction vessels/towers etc.

**Key points**
- Learn the four equations.
- Learn the conditions for each stage – temperature, pressure, catalyst.

The details of the reaction containers are not important.

This reaction is a reversible reaction.

SO$_3$ cannot safely be dissolved in water because a 'fog' of sulphuric acid droplets form.

Therefore . . .
SO$_3$ is dissolved in conc. H$_2$SO$_4$ . . .

. . . and then diluted with water.

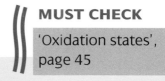
**MUST CHECK**
'Oxidation states',
page 45

### WORKED EXAMPLE

Give the names and formulae of the compounds of sulphur that are formed during the manufacture of sulphuric acid.

Show how the oxidation state of sulphur changes during the process, starting from elemental sulphur.

| Name | Formula | Oxidation state of sulphur | |
|------|---------|---------------------------|---|
| | | Calculation | Value |
| sulphur | S | | 0 |
| sulphur dioxide | SO$_2$ | [+4 − 2(−2) = 0] | +4 |
| sulphur trioxide | SO$_3$ | [+6 + 3(−2) = 0] | +6 |
| oleum | H$_2$S$_2$O$_7$ | [2(+1) + 2(+6) + 7(−2) = 0] | +6 |
| concentrated sulphuric acid | H$_2$SO$_4$ | [2(+1) + (+6) + 4(−2) = 0] | +6 |

# CHOOSING THE CONDITIONS FOR THE CONVERTER

The reaction in the converter operates under 'compromise' conditions to:

- give a reasonable yield
- at a fast rate.

A high temperature increases the reaction rate.

Vanadium(V) oxide catalyst:

- increases the rate
- has no effect on the yield.

Converter
450–600°C, 10 atm pressure
$V_2O_5$ catalyst

$$SO_2(g) + \tfrac{1}{2}O_2(g) \rightleftharpoons SO_3(g)$$

The reaction is exothermic ($\Delta H$ is negative).
Therefore a high temperature:

- favours the endothermic reaction (reverse reaction)
- reduces yield

BUT . . .

- gives a faster rate → compromise!

$\Delta H = -98$ kJ mol$^{-1}$

$1\tfrac{1}{2}$ gas molecules    1 gas molecule

Fewer gas molecules on the right.
Therefore a higher pressure:

- moves equilibrium to the right
- increases yield

AND ALSO . . .

- increases the rate!

**What happens to unreacted $SO_2$ and $O_2$?**
Unreacted gases are recycled back in to give a higher percentage conversion.

## WHY MAKING SULPHURIC ACID IS IMPORTANT

Sulphuric acid is used to make a very wide range of everyday chemical products.

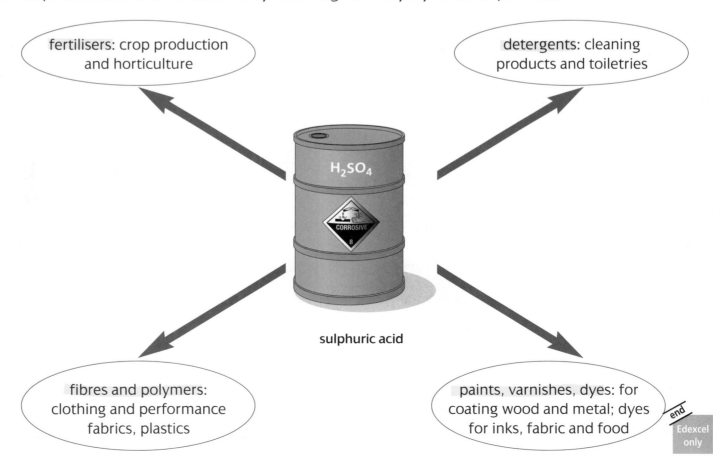

fertilisers: crop production and horticulture

detergents: cleaning products and toiletries

$H_2SO_4$

CORROSIVE
8

sulphuric acid

fibres and polymers: clothing and performance fabrics, plastics

paints, varnishes, dyes: for coating wood and metal; dyes for inks, fabric and food

end

# ELECTROLYSIS OF SODIUM CHLORIDE

start
Edexcel only

## THE MEMBRANE CELL

A membrane cell is used to electrolyse brine – sodium chloride solution.

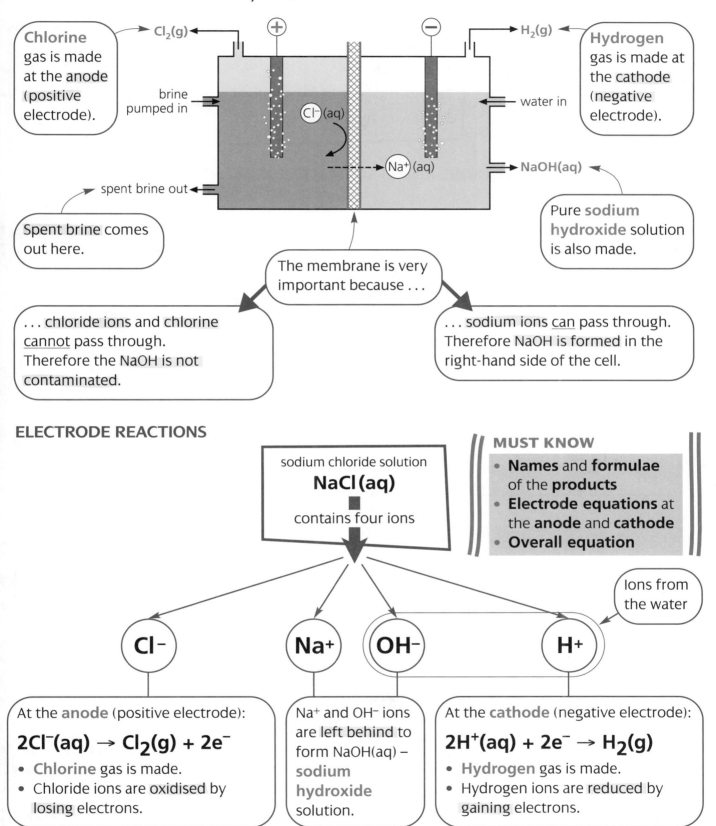

**Chlorine** gas is made at the anode (positive electrode).

**Hydrogen** gas is made at the cathode (negative electrode).

brine pumped in

water in

Spent brine comes out here.

Pure **sodium hydroxide** solution is also made.

The membrane is very important because . . .

. . . chloride ions and chlorine cannot pass through. Therefore the NaOH is not contaminated.

. . . sodium ions can pass through. Therefore NaOH is formed in the right-hand side of the cell.

## ELECTRODE REACTIONS

sodium chloride solution
**NaCl(aq)**
contains four ions

**MUST KNOW**
- **Names** and **formulae** of the **products**
- **Electrode equations** at the **anode** and **cathode**
- **Overall equation**

Ions from the water

**Cl⁻**   **Na⁺**   **OH⁻**   **H⁺**

At the **anode** (positive electrode):
$$2Cl^-(aq) \rightarrow Cl_2(g) + 2e^-$$
- **Chlorine** gas is made.
- Chloride ions are oxidised by losing electrons.

Na⁺ and OH⁻ ions are left behind to form NaOH(aq) – **sodium hydroxide** solution.

At the **cathode** (negative electrode):
$$2H^+(aq) + 2e^- \rightarrow H_2(g)$$
- **Hydrogen** gas is made.
- Hydrogen ions are reduced by gaining electrons.

**Overall equation**
$$2NaCl(aq) + 2H_2O(l) \rightarrow Cl_2(g) + H_2(g) + 2NaOH(aq)$$

# WHY THE ELECTROLYSIS OF SODIUM CHLORIDE IS IMPORTANT

- **Electrolysis** uses a cheap raw material – common salt, NaCl – to produce four important industrial chemicals.
- The main cost of the process is the extraction costs and the fuel costs for the electrolysis.

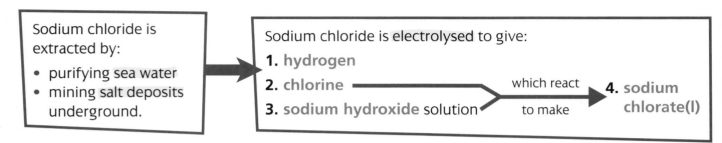

Sodium chloride is extracted by:
- purifying sea water
- mining salt deposits underground.

Sodium chloride is electrolysed to give:
1. **hydrogen**
2. **chlorine** ————— which react
3. **sodium hydroxide** solution —— to make
4. **sodium chlorate(I)**

## REACTION BETWEEN CHLORINE AND SODIUM HYDROXIDE SOLUTION

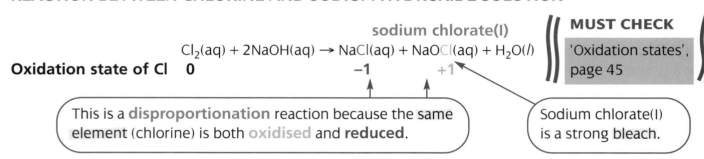

sodium chlorate(I)

$$Cl_2(aq) + 2NaOH(aq) \rightarrow NaCl(aq) + NaOCl(aq) + H_2O(l)$$

**Oxidation state of Cl**   0                          –1          +1

This is a **disproportionation** reaction because the **same** element (chlorine) is both **oxidised** and **reduced**.

Sodium chlorate(I) is a strong **bleach**.

**MUST CHECK**

'Oxidation states', page 45

## WHAT THE PRODUCTS ARE USED FOR

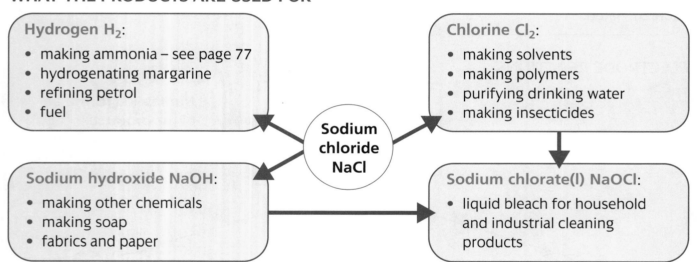

**Hydrogen H$_2$:**
- making ammonia – see page 77
- hydrogenating margarine
- refining petrol
- fuel

**Chlorine Cl$_2$:**
- making solvents
- making polymers
- purifying drinking water
- making insecticides

**Sodium** **chloride** **NaCl**

**Sodium hydroxide NaOH:**
- making other chemicals
- making soap
- fabrics and paper

**Sodium chlorate(I) NaOCl:**
- liquid bleach for household and industrial cleaning products

**WORKED EXAMPLE**

A student electrolysed an aqueous solution of sodium chloride containing a few drops of Universal Indicator (UI) solution. He made the following observations:

(a) Bubbles of gas formed at both electrodes.
(b) The UI solution turned dark blue around the cathode.
(c) The UI solution turned red around the anode then, after a few minutes, turned colourless.

Outline the reactions that caused these changes.

(a) Bubbles of gas formed at both electrodes because **chlorine** gas forms at the anode, and **hydrogen** gas forms at the cathode.
   **At the anode** $2Cl^-(aq) \rightarrow Cl_2(g) + 2e^-$     **At the cathode** $2H^+(aq) + 2e^- \rightarrow H_2(g)$
(b) UI turned dark blue as **aqueous sodium hydroxide** (a strong alkali) forms.
(c) **Chlorine** gas dissolving in the water around the cathode turned the UI red then colourless.

**MUST CHECK**

The reaction between **chlorine** and **water**, page 50

end
Edexcel only

# THE BLAST FURNACE

start
AQA only

## WHAT HAPPENS IN THE BLAST FURNACE?

**Limestone:**
- thermally decomposes to form CaO ('lime' or calcium oxide)
- which removes silicon dioxide impurities as slag

**Coke:**
- contains mainly carbon
- burns and heats the furnace
- reacts to form carbon monoxide
- C and CO are the reducing agents in the furnace

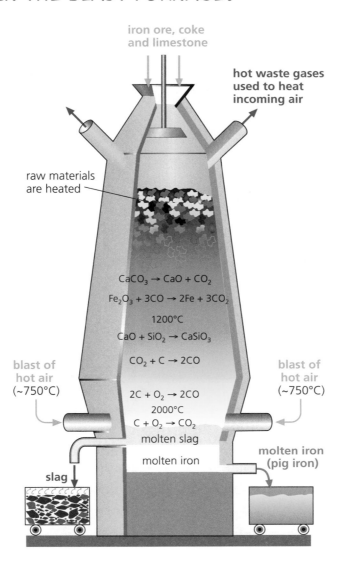

iron ore, coke and limestone

hot waste gases used to heat incoming air

raw materials are heated

$CaCO_3 \rightarrow CaO + CO_2$

$Fe_2O_3 + 3CO \rightarrow 2Fe + 3CO_2$

1200°C

$CaO + SiO_2 \rightarrow CaSiO_3$

$CO_2 + C \rightarrow 2CO$

$2C + O_2 \rightarrow 2CO$

2000°C

$C + O_2 \rightarrow CO_2$

molten slag

molten iron

blast of hot air (~750°C)

blast of hot air (~750°C)

molten iron (pig iron)

slag

**Iron oxide:**
- is the main compound in iron ore
- iron in iron oxide is reduced by CO
- molten iron is 'tapped off' at the bottom

**Air:**
- is blasted in at the bottom
- reacts with the carbon

## WHY THE BLAST FURNACE IS A CONTINUOUS PROCESS

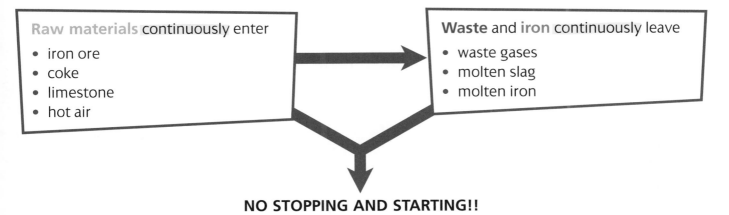

**Raw materials** continuously enter
- iron ore
- coke
- limestone
- hot air

**Waste** and iron continuously leave
- waste gases
- molten slag
- molten iron

**NO STOPPING AND STARTING!!**

Advantages of using a continuous process:

- The furnace runs day and night – no unproductive time so more iron made per day.
- Less energy is wasted by allowing it to cool and then reheating from cold.
- Materials in and out can be automatically controlled at optimum rates.

# A CLOSER LOOK AT THE EQUATIONS

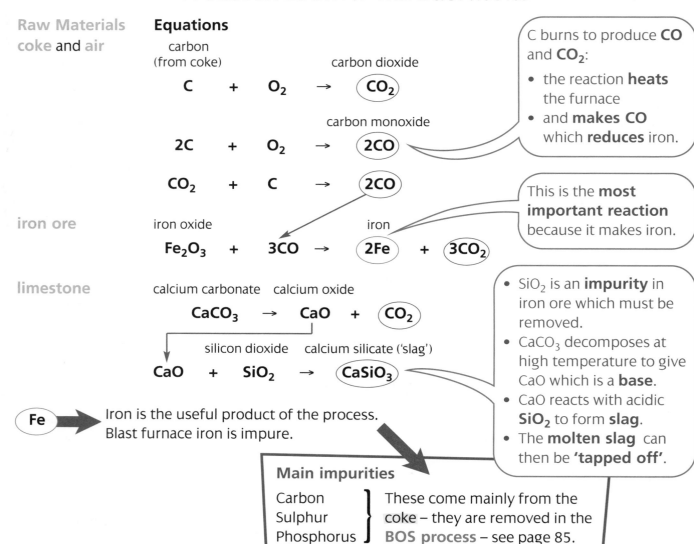

**Raw Materials**
**coke** and **air**

**Equations**

carbon
(from coke)                                    carbon dioxide

$$C + O_2 \rightarrow \boxed{CO_2}$$

carbon monoxide

$$2C + O_2 \rightarrow \boxed{2CO}$$

$$CO_2 + C \rightarrow \boxed{2CO}$$

**iron ore**

iron oxide                                          iron

$$Fe_2O_3 + 3CO \rightarrow \boxed{2Fe} + \boxed{3CO_2}$$

**limestone**

calcium carbonate    calcium oxide

$$CaCO_3 \rightarrow CaO + \boxed{CO_2}$$

silicon dioxide    calcium silicate ('slag')

$$CaO + SiO_2 \rightarrow \boxed{CaSiO_3}$$

> C burns to produce **CO** and **CO₂**:
> • the reaction **heats** the furnace
> • and **makes CO** which **reduces** iron.

> This is the **most important reaction** because it makes iron.

> • $SiO_2$ is an **impurity** in iron ore which must be removed.
> • $CaCO_3$ decomposes at high temperature to give CaO which is a **base**.
> • CaO reacts with acidic $SiO_2$ to form **slag**.
> • The **molten slag** can then be **'tapped off'**.

**Fe** → Iron is the useful product of the process. Blast furnace iron is impure.

**Main impurities**

Carbon
Sulphur    } These come mainly from the **coke** – they are removed in the
Phosphorus    **BOS process** – see page 85.

## DEALING WITH THE WASTE

| Waste products | ... formed when ... | ... cause problems ... | ... which are solved by ... |
|---|---|---|---|
| $CO_2$ | carbon burns | relatively harmless, but could suffocate workers | collecting gases at top of furnace |
| CO | carbon reacts in the furnace | toxic, inhibits oxygen transport in the blood | collecting and using as a fuel to heat other areas of the plant |
| $SO_2$ | sulphur impurities in the coke burn | acid rain, breathing difficulties | collecting and 'scrubbing' waste gases to remove $SO_2$ |
| $CaSiO_3$ (slag) | silicon dioxide is removed | solid when cool, formed in very large quantities | using as a 'filler' under motorways and roads |

## WORKED EXAMPLE

(a) Write an equation to show the reaction that reduces iron in the blast furnace.
(b) Use oxidation states to show that this is a redox reaction and identify the reducing agent.

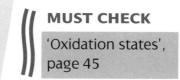

**MUST CHECK**

'Oxidation states', page 45

(a)
$$Fe_2O_3 + 3CO \rightarrow 2Fe + 3CO_2$$

(b) Oxidation states   $2(+3) + 3(-2) = 0$   $+2 + (-2) = 0$   $0$   $+4 + 2(-2) = 0$

This is a redox reaction because iron is **reduced** (from oxidation state +3 to 0), and carbon is oxidised (from oxidation state +2 to +4).
The **reducing agent** is carbon in carbon monoxide.

end

AQA only

# MAKING STEEL

start

**AQA only**

## THE BOS PROCESS

Iron from the blast furnace contains impurities including carbon, phosphorus and sulphur.
These are removed in the **B**asic **O**xygen **S**teelmaking process (**BOS process**) in a container called a converter.

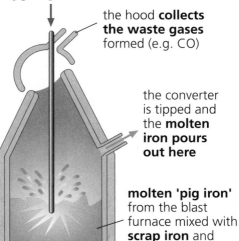

**oxygen** goes in here

the hood **collects the waste gases** formed (e.g. CO)

the converter is tipped and the **molten iron pours out here**

molten 'pig iron' from the blast furnace mixed with **scrap iron** and **calcium oxide**

### Step 1: Removal of sulphur

- Hundreds of kg of **magnesium powder** are injected into the molten iron.
- A very exothermic reaction happens:

  $Mg + S \rightarrow MgS$

- **Magnesium sulphide** floats to the top and is **raked off**.

**Scrap iron** is used:
- to **recycle** used iron
- as a **coolant** to stop the furnace **overheating** – the reactions are all **exothermic**.

### Step 2: Oxygen blow

- **Oxygen** is blown onto the surface of the molten iron.
- **Carbon** and **phosphorus** are **oxidised** to form oxides.

**Carbon**   $2C + O_2 \rightarrow 2CO$

Carbon monoxide is a gas:
- It is collected in the hood at the top of the converter.

**Calcium oxide** makes **slag** with **acidic oxide impurities**.

**Phosphorus**   $4P + 5O_2 \rightarrow P_4O_{10}$

$P_4O_{10}$ is an acidic oxide:
- It reacts with calcium oxide to form a slag.
- The slag floats to the top and is raked off.

## MAKING STEEL

- Iron from the converter is used to make steel.
- Steel is iron that has been alloyed (mixed) with small amounts of other added elements.
- Different types of steel contain different elements, e.g.:
  - mild steel contains carbon
  - stainless steel contains chromium.

---

**WORKED EXAMPLE**

The equations show the reactions that remove the impurities sulphur and phosphorus from molten iron.

$$Mg + S \rightarrow MgS \qquad\qquad 4P + 5O_2 \rightarrow P_4O_{10}$$

Show, by the use of oxidation states, which impure element has been oxidised and which has been reduced.

$$Mg + S \rightarrow MgS \qquad\qquad 4P + 5O_2 \rightarrow P_4O_{10}$$

Oxidation states    0   **0**    +2  –2       0    **0**    $4[Ox]P + 10(-2) = 0$

$$4[Ox]P = +20$$
$$[Ox]P = +5$$

**Sulphur** is **reduced** (oxidation state decreases from 0 to –2) and phosphorus is oxidised (oxidation state increases from 0 to +5) in the reactions.

end

**AQA only**

# EXTRACTING REACTIVE METALS

## HOW REACTIVE METALS ARE EXTRACTED

Metals of low to medium reactivity (e.g. iron) can be extracted from their compounds by heating with coke (carbon).

Reduction by carbon cannot be used to extract more reactive metals from their compounds because:
- very reactive metal ions need a very powerful reducing agent to reduce them
- other reactions take place to form metal–carbon compounds (metal carbides)
- it takes much more energy to extract more reactive metals.

More powerful reducing agents are needed e.g. **titanium** is extracted using Mg or Na.

Therefore . . .

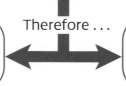

**Electrolysis** can be used to overcome the high energy demand e.g. **aluminium extraction**. (See page 87.)

## EXTRACTING TITANIUM

start AQA only

Titanium is an important metal because it is very light and corrosion resistant – it is used to make airborne transport and satellites.

**Step 1:** 'Rutile' ore contains **titanium oxide** which is reacted with **chlorine** and **carbon** to make **titanium(IV) chloride**.

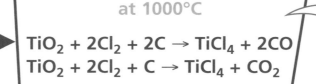

at 1000°C

$$TiO_2 + 2Cl_2 + 2C \rightarrow TiCl_4 + 2CO$$
$$TiO_2 + 2Cl_2 + C \rightarrow TiCl_4 + CO_2$$

**CO and $CO_2$** are made – same as in the blast furnace. **CO is toxic** so must be collected and piped away.

**Step 2:** Titanium(IV) chloride is **reduced** using either **magnesium** or **sodium**.

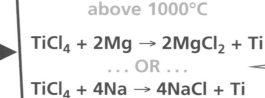

above 1000°C

$$TiCl_4 + 2Mg \rightarrow 2MgCl_2 + Ti$$
. . . OR . . .
$$TiCl_4 + 4Na \rightarrow 4NaCl + Ti$$

Mg and Na are able to **reduce** Ti by **displacement** because they are **more reactive** than Ti.

### Batch Processes
- This process happens in a **batch process**. The reactants are mixed and left until the reaction is finished – reactants and products do not flow in and out.
- This is because:
  – the reaction is slow – it is left for about 2 days
  – the mixture is monitored until enough product is formed before the container is emptied.

**MUST CHECK**

Compare this **batch process** to a **continuous process** – see 'The blast furnace', page 83.

### WORKED EXAMPLE
Titanium oxide occurs naturally in very large amounts, yet the cost of titanium is very high. Explain why extracting titanium is so expensive.

Extracting titanium uses **large amounts of chlorine** and either **sodium** or **magnesium**. These are not available as cheap raw materials. They are **expensive elements**, each of which is extracted using **electrolysis**.
The process is expensive because it uses a **high temperature** (hence high fuel costs) and is a **slow batch process**, taking several days.

end AQA only

# EXTRACTING ALUMINIUM

## STAGES IN EXTRACTING ALUMINIUM

**Step 1: Mining**
**Bauxite** ore is mined. It contains:

- mainly **aluminium oxide**, $Al_2O_3$
- with **other oxide impurities** – iron(III) oxide, silicon dioxide.

**Step 2: Purification**
**Bauxite** is purified by:

- dissolving in hot sodium hydroxide solution, NaOH(aq)
  - $Al_2O_3$ dissolves
  - impurities do not dissolve
- filtering to remove impurities
- cooling to precipitate pure $Al_2O_3$

### Step 3: Electrolysis

At the **anode (positive electrode)**

- **oxygen** forms:
  $2O^{2-} \rightarrow O_2 + 4e^-$
- oxygen reacts with the carbon anode to form **carbon dioxide**:
  $C + O_2 \rightarrow CO_2$

- **Hot oxygen** is formed – it is **very reactive**, so needs to be removed.
- The **carbon anode reacts** with the oxygen to form **unreactive carbon dioxide**.
- This reaction **uses up the anode**, so it needs to be continually replaced.

At the **cathode (negative electrode)**

- **aluminium** forms:
  $Al^{3+} + 3e^- \rightarrow Al$

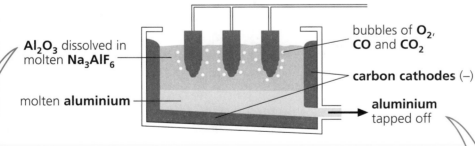

**carbon anodes** (+)

$Al_2O_3$ dissolved in molten **$Na_3AlF_6$**

molten **aluminium**

bubbles of **$O_2$**, **CO** and **$CO_2$**

**carbon cathodes** (–)

**aluminium** tapped off

$Al_2O_3$ is dissolved in **molten cryolite** ($Na_3AlF_6$) because:

- the **melting point** of pure $Al_2O_3$ is very high (2015°C)
- $Al_2O_3$ dissolved in cryolite is molten at a **much lower temperature** (900°C)
- a lower temperature process has **lower fuel costs** and is much **safer** to run.

- **Aluminium** forms at the cathode and is tapped off as a **very hot liquid**.
- Aluminium is **reduced** as it gains electrons in the reaction.

# EXTRACTION VERSUS RECYCLING

- Although **bauxite** is naturally abundant, aluminium is a **very expensive** metal.
- This is mainly due to the very high energy costs involved in the electrolysis.
- It takes much less energy to recycle aluminium.

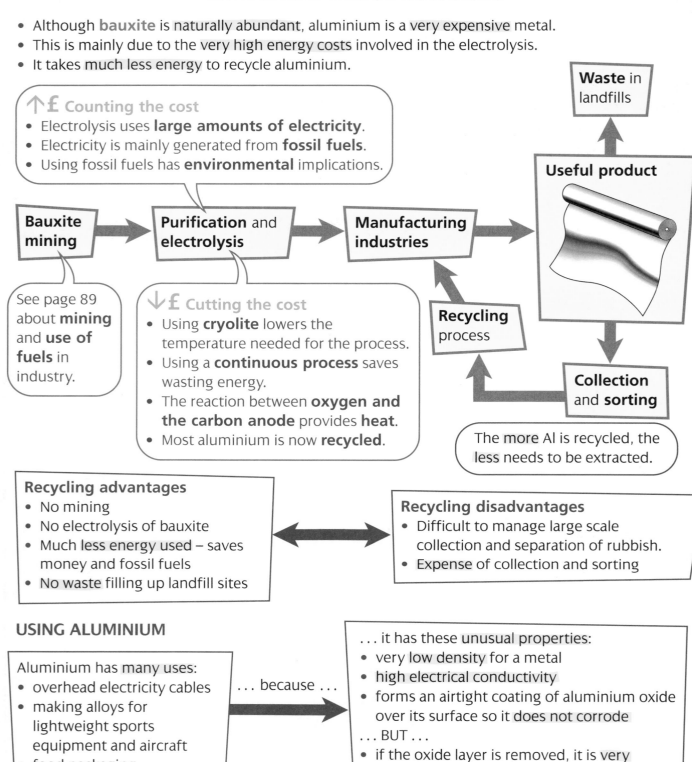

**↑£ Counting the cost**
- Electrolysis uses **large amounts of electricity**.
- Electricity is mainly generated from **fossil fuels**.
- Using fossil fuels has **environmental** implications.

**Bauxite mining** → **Purification** and **electrolysis** → **Manufacturing industries** →

**Waste** in landfills

**Useful product**

See page 89 about **mining** and **use of fuels** in industry.

**↓£ Cutting the cost**
- Using **cryolite** lowers the temperature needed for the process.
- Using a **continuous process** saves wasting energy.
- The reaction between **oxygen and the carbon anode** provides **heat**.
- Most aluminium is now **recycled**.

**Recycling** process

**Collection** and **sorting**

The more Al is recycled, the less needs to be extracted.

**Recycling advantages**
- No mining
- No electrolysis of bauxite
- Much less energy used – saves money and fossil fuels
- No waste filling up landfill sites

**Recycling disadvantages**
- Difficult to manage large scale collection and separation of rubbish.
- Expense of collection and sorting

## USING ALUMINIUM

Aluminium has many uses:
- overhead electricity cables
- making alloys for lightweight sports equipment and aircraft
- food packaging

. . . because . . .

. . . it has these unusual properties:
- very low density for a metal
- high electrical conductivity
- forms an airtight coating of aluminium oxide over its surface so it does not corrode
. . . BUT . . .
- if the oxide layer is removed, it is very reactive!

### WORKED EXAMPLE

Describe, using equations, the reactions that happen at the anode during the electrolysis of bauxite. Give reasons why these reactions are important to the process.

At the anode, oxygen ions **lose electrons** to form oxygen gas: $2O^{2-} \rightarrow O_2 + 4e^-$

Oxygen gas reacts with the **carbon anode** to form carbon dioxide: $C + O_2 \rightarrow CO_2$

If asked to **'describe'**, use **equations and words**.

These reactions are important because they **remove** the very reactive, hot **oxygen** gas before it reacts with the steel tank or molten aluminium. The oxidation of carbon is very **exothermic** – this **provides heat**, which is needed to keep the process at 900°C.

end

Edexcel and AQA only

# INDUSTRY AND ENVIRONMENT

start

Edexcel and AQA only

## MINING

| Mining causes these problems ... | ... which can be minimised by ... |
|---|---|
| • **destruction** of landscape and habitats | • old mines being given **new uses** – leisure or landfill |
| • **dust**, **noise** | • **water spraying** and creating **banks** to cut down the noise and dust |
| • some mined resources are **finite** – will run out | • **recycling** to conserve resources |
| • **large-scale transport** of mined materials uses **large quantities of fuel** and **increases** land and sea **traffic** | • building processing plants **near** mines to cut transport needs |
| • large amounts of waste rock | • using waste rock as hard core for roads and building |

## INDUSTRY AND ENERGY

**Examples**

$NH_3$ • **Haber process** – page 77

• **Contact process** – page 79  $H_2SO_4$

$Fe$ • **Blast furnace** – page 83

• **Aluminium extraction** – page 87  $Al$

Most of our electricity is generated from fossil fuels:

• Fossil fuels are coal, gas and oil.

• Fossil fuels are finite and will run out.

• They produce pollutant gases when they burn.

• They need to be conserved for making chemicals – e.g. polymers and detergents (see page 113).

**HIGH TEMPERATURE PROCESSES**
Use large amounts of energy

300°C  1200°C  1000°C  600°C

£ € Using large amounts of energy is very expensive. $

Burning fuels gives out harmful waste gases (see next page).

• Waste gases must be collected for two reasons:
  – health and safety of the workers at the plant
  – industrial plants are not allowed to release harmful gases into the air.

Energy demand is reduced by:

• using catalysts to give faster rates at lower temperatures

• using continuous processes so less energy is wasted.

The use of fossil fuels is reduced by:

• using alternative/renewable fuels e.g. old car tyres, woodchips.

Alternative sources, such as solar and wind power, do not produce enough energy fast enough for large-scale industrial processes.

# DEALING WITH THE WASTE

## COMMON WASTE GASES

| This gas ... | ... is formed when ... | ... and causes ... |
|---|---|---|
| **sulphur dioxide** $SO_2$ | • **sulphur impurities** in fuels burn ... and ... <br> • **metals** are extracted from **metal sulphide** ores | • **breathing problems** <br> • **acid rain** |
| **carbon dioxide** $CO_2$ | • fuels burn | • can cause **suffocation** if it builds up inside buildings (i.e. no oxygen) <br> • increase in the **greenhouse effect** |
| **carbon monoxide** CO | • **incomplete combustion** happens <br> • iron is extracted in a **blast furnace** | • **blocks oxygen transport** in the blood – forms carboxyhaemoglobin |

Therefore ...

- $SO_2$ can be scrubbed out of waste gases using filters made from limestone.
- $CO_2$ is collected and released into the air, but governments and industry are working to reduce emissions by increasing fuel efficiency and using non-fossil fuels.
- CO is collected and is burned as a fuel:
  $2CO + O_2 \rightarrow 2CO_2$

## SOLID WASTE

For example:
- slag from processes such as the blast furnace
- solid waste rock from separation of metal ores after mining

→

- Waste slag heaps can be covered with topsoil, planted and used for leisure.
- Crushed waste slag is used as a filler for building and road foundations.

## PRESSURE AND CATALYSTS

Both increasing the **pressure** and using a **catalyst** can increase the rate of industrial processes. This means that they can run at lower temperatures.

| Increasing the pressure ... | | Using a catalyst ... | |
|---|---|---|---|
| **+** | **−** | **+** | **−** |
| ⊕ increases the **rate** <br> ⊕ increases the **yield** for some reactions | ⊖ is **expensive** to set up and maintain as leaks from higher pressure processes are more likely <br> ⊖ increases **health and safety** risks | ⊕ increases the **rate** <br> ⊕ has a very **low running cost** because the same catalyst **can be re-used** indefinitely | ⊖ **high** initial purchase **price** <br> ⊖ reactants must be 'clean' to prevent contamination or **poisoning** of the catalyst surface |

### WORKED EXAMPLE

Waste gases are collected and piped away from the top of a blast furnace.
Explain why this is necessary for the health and safety of the workers.

Blast furnace waste gas contains three gases that are potentially harmful.
1. **Carbon dioxide** could cause suffocation to workers around the furnace as it is **denser than air** and so could **collect and replace the air** at ground level.
2. **Carbon monoxide** is toxic as it forms carboxyhaemoglobin in the blood, **stopping the transport of oxygen** by haemoglobin, resulting in suffocation.
3. **Sulphur dioxide** is **very acidic** and causes **breathing difficulties**.

end

Edexcel and AQA only

# NAMING ORGANIC MOLECULES

## SIMPLE ORGANIC MOLECULES

### HYDROCARBONS

Alkanes and alkenes are hydrocarbons because they contain hydrogen and carbon only.

### Alkanes

**General formula: $C_nH_{(2n+2)}$**

e.g. ethane

| Name | Number of C atoms | Structural formula |
|---|---|---|
| methane | 1 | $CH_4$ |
| ethane | 2 | $CH_3CH_3$ |
| propane | 3 | $CH_3CH_2CH_3$ |
| butane | 4 | $CH_3CH_2CH_2CH_3$ |
| pentane | 5 | $CH_3CH_2CH_2CH_2CH_3$ |
| hexane | 6 | $CH_3CH_2CH_2CH_2CH_2CH_3$ |

The **beginning of the name** shows **how many C atoms** are in the formula e.g. 'pent' = 5.

### Alkenes

**General formula: $C_nH_{2n}$**

e.g. ethene

| Name | Number of C atoms | Structural formula |
|---|---|---|
| ethene | 2 | $CH_2=CH_2$ |
| propene | 3 | $CH_3CH=CH_2$ |
| but-1-ene | 4 | $CH_3CH_2CH=CH_2$ |
| pent-1-ene | 5 | $CH_3CH_2CH_2CH=CH_2$ |
| hex-1-ene | 6 | $CH_3CH_2CH_2CH_2CH=CH_2$ |

The **end of the names** shows the **type of compound** e.g. 'ene' compounds have a double bond.

**Numbers** – see next page

## OTHER ORGANIC MOLECULES

Most organic molecules consist of an **alkyl group** attached to **functional groups**.

Alkyl group **R** — **X** Functional group

### Functional groups

| Type of compound | Functional group | Compound name ends with |
|---|---|---|
| alcohol | –OH | . . . ol |
| carboxylic acid | –COOH | . . . oic acid |

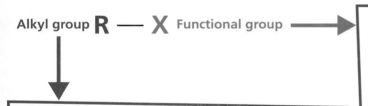

$CH_3OH$  Name: methanol

$C_3H_7COOH$  Name: butanoic acid

four C atoms = 'butan . . .'

### Alkyl groups

| Name of group | Formula | Number of C atoms | Compound name starts with |
|---|---|---|---|
| methyl | $CH_3$ | 1 | methan . . . |
| ethyl | $C_2H_5$ | 2 | ethan . . . |
| propyl | $C_3H_7$ | 3 | propan . . . |
| butyl | $C_4H_9$ | 4 | butan . . . |
| pentyl | $C_5H_{11}$ | 5 | pentan . . . |
| hexyl | $C_6H_{13}$ | 6 | hexan . . . |

Notice the **same name beginnings**.

# SHOWING THE POSITION OF FUNCTIONAL GROUPS

## RULES

1. Numbers in names show **which carbon atom** has the functional group attached.
2. Start from the end of the molecule that gives the **lowest number** (see Example 1).
3. If there is more than one **different functional group**, name them in **alphabetical order** (see Example 2).
4. If there is more than one of the **same functional group**, use the prefixes:
   di = 2  (see Example 3)  tri = 3
5. For branched chains, use the **longest chain** to name the compound (see Example 4).

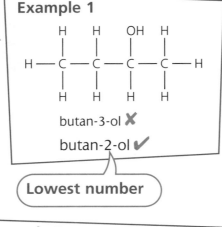

**Example 1**

butan-3-ol ✗

butan-2-ol ✔

Lowest number

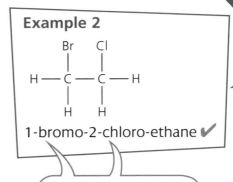

**Example 2**

1-bromo-2-chloro-ethane ✔

Alphabetical order

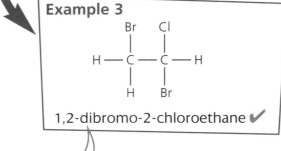

**Example 3**

1,2-dibromo-2-chloroethane ✔

Two Br atoms

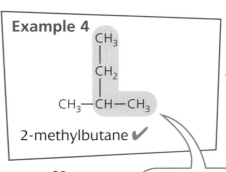

**Example 4**

2-methylbutane ✔

**Longest chain** is four C atoms = **'butane'**

**MUST TAKE CARE**
- **Commas** between numbers
- **Dashes** everywhere else!

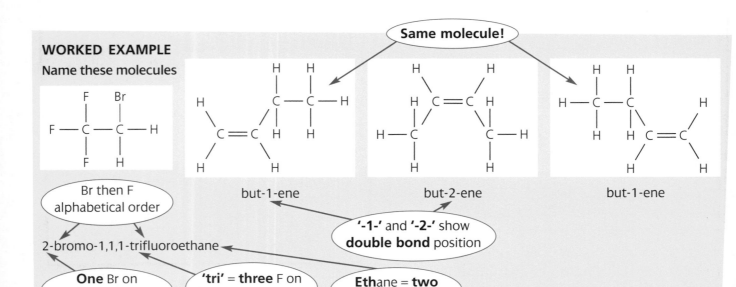

**Same molecule!**

**WORKED EXAMPLE**
Name these molecules

but-1-ene

but-2-ene

but-1-ene

Br then F
alphabetical order

2-bromo-1,1,1-trifluoroethane

**'-1-'** and **'-2-'** show **double bond** position

**One** Br on **second (2)** carbon

**'tri'** = **three** F on **first** carbon (**1,1,1**)

**Eth**ane = **two** Cs altogether

# FORMULAE AND STRUCTURE

## SIMPLE FORMULAE
### EMPIRICAL AND MOLECULAR FORMULAE

**MUST CHECK**
'Empirical and molecular formulae', page 11

**Key ideas**
- The **molecular formula** shows the actual number of atoms present in a molecule.
- The **empirical formula** is the simplest whole-number ratio of the number of atoms of each element in the compound.

**Ethane**

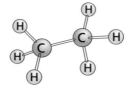

Molecular formula: $C_2H_6$

Empirical formula: $CH_3$

**Ethanoic acid**

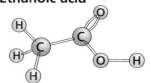

Molecular formula: $C_2H_4O_2$

Empirical formula: $CH_2O$

## STRUCTURAL FORMULAE AND DISPLAYED FORMULAE

**Key ideas**
- The **structural formula** shows the position and types of **functional groups** (including double or triple bonds) in a molecule.
- The **displayed formula** (sometimes called **full structural formula**) shows **every atom** and **every bond**.

**Propene**

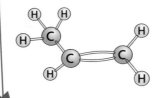

Structural formula: $CH_3CH=CH_2$

Displayed formula:

**Single bonds** are **not shown** in structural formulae.

**Double bond**

Show **every bond** but draw the molecule flat.

**or**

**Propan-2-ol**

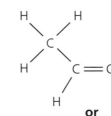

Show position of **OH** group

Structural formula: $CH_3CH(OH)CH_3$

Displayed formula:

Show **every bond**

## STRUCTURES OF COMMON FUNCTIONAL GROUPS

|  | Structural formula | Displayed formula |
|---|---|---|
| Hydroxyl group (in alcohols) | OH | —O—H |
| Carboxylic acid group | COOH | |

**Don't lose marks!**
Show **every bond** in displayed formulae – even between O and H.

# SKELETAL FORMULAE

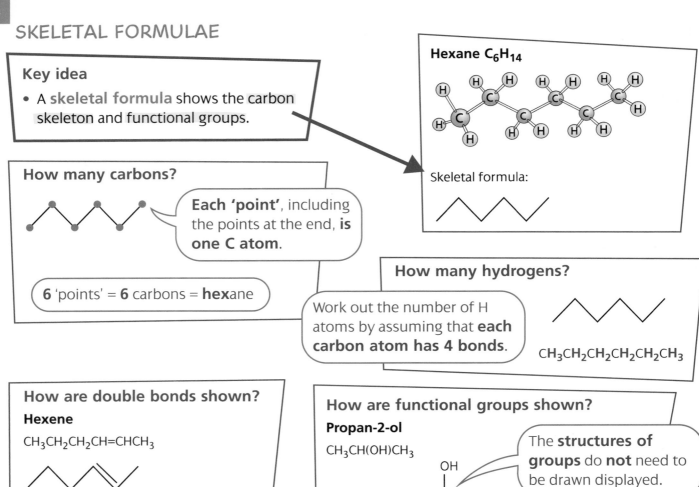

## Key idea

- A **skeletal formula** shows the **carbon** skeleton and functional groups.

**Hexane C₆H₁₄**

Skeletal formula:

## How many carbons?

Each 'point', including the points at the end, **is one C atom**.

6 'points' = **6** carbons = **hex**ane

## How many hydrogens?

Work out the number of H atoms by assuming that **each carbon atom has 4 bonds**.

CH₃CH₂CH₂CH₂CH₂CH₃

## How are double bonds shown?

**Hexene**

CH₃CH₂CH₂CH=CHCH₃

## How are functional groups shown?

**Propan-2-ol**

CH₃CH(OH)CH₃

OH

The **structures of groups** do **not** need to be drawn displayed.

## WORKED EXAMPLE

Write displayed, structural and molecular formulae for the following compounds which are represented by their skeletal formulae.

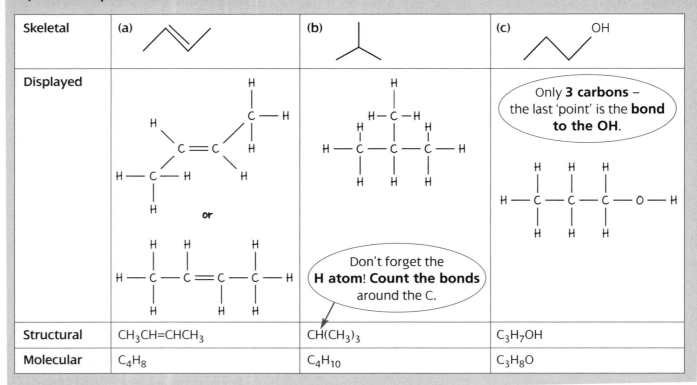

| Skeletal | (a) | (b) | (c) OH |
|---|---|---|---|
| Displayed | | | Only **3 carbons** – the last 'point' is the **bond to the OH**. |
| | or | Don't forget the **H atom! Count the bonds** around the C. | |
| Structural | CH₃CH=CHCH₃ | CH(CH₃)₃ | C₃H₇OH |
| Molecular | C₄H₈ | C₄H₁₀ | C₃H₈O |

# ISOMERS

## WHAT ARE ISOMERS?

Isomers are molecules with the same molecular formulae but a different arrangement of atoms.

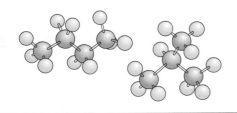

**2** types of isomers

Structural isomers

Geometric isomers (stereoisomers)

## STRUCTURAL ISOMERS

- There are **3** types of structural isomers.
- Structural isomers have **different names** from each other.

Structural isomers have the same molecular formulae but their atoms are arranged in a different order.

### Chain isomers

- The carbon chain is arranged differently.

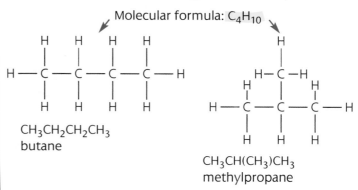

Molecular formula: $C_4H_{10}$

$CH_3CH_2CH_2CH_3$
butane

$CH_3CH(CH_3)CH_3$
methylpropane

- Chain isomers have **different physical properties** – e.g. **different boiling points**.

### Position isomers

- The **position of functional groups** is different.

Molecular formula: $C_3H_7Cl$

$CH_3CH_2CH_2Cl$
1-chloropropane

$CH_3CHClCH_3$
2-chloropropane

### Functional group isomers

- The atoms are arranged differently to give **different functional groups**.

Molecular formula: $C_3H_8O$

Different functional groups

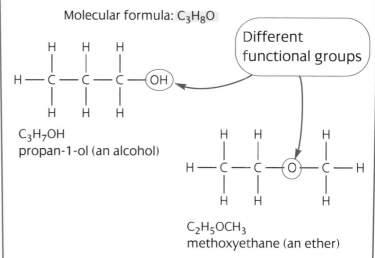

$C_3H_7OH$
propan-1-ol (an alcohol)

$C_2H_5OCH_3$
methoxyethane (an ether)

- Functional group isomers have **different physical and chemical properties**.

**MUST REMEMBER**
- **Backwards**, **upside down** or **bent** molecules are not isomers!

# GEOMETRIC ISOMERS

## 5 KEY POINTS ABOUT GEOMETRIC ISOMERS

- They have the same molecular formulae AND the atoms are bonded in the same order.
- BUT . . . the atoms are arranged differently in space.
- Molecules must have a double bond.
- Atoms cannot rotate about the double bond – it is fixed.
- Geometric isomers cannot be superimposed on one another.

double bond

no rotation

bond is **fixed**

## Geometric isomers of but-1-ene

$H_3C$ $CH_3$
C=C
H H

Melting point 139°C

Both methyl groups point up – same side.

$H_3C$ H
C=C
H $CH_3$

Melting point 105°C

One methyl group points up, one points down – opposite sides.

Geometric isomers have different **physical properties** – e.g. melting and boiling points, density.

The groups **cannot change places** because the double bond **cannot rotate**.

## CIS AND TRANS ISOMERS

- *cis* means 'on the same side' of the double bond.
- *trans* means 'on the opposite side' of the double bond.

*cis* = both Br atoms on **same side** of double bond

Br Br
C=C
H H

***cis*-1,2-dibromoethane**

Br H
C=C
H Br

***trans*-1,2-dibromoethane**

*trans* = Br atoms on **different sides** of double bond

## WORKED EXAMPLE

From the molecules A to D, identify two different isomers of pentane. Explain your reasoning.

Remember molecules are **3-D** and **move about!**

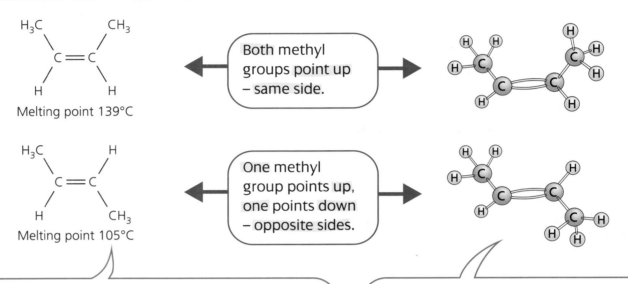

Pentane

A          B          C          D

B (or D) and C are different isomers. A is **the same as pentane**. It has been drawn **bent** but the atoms are in the **same order**: $CH_3CH_2CH_2CH_2CH_3$. B and D are the **same molecule**, D is drawn **backwards**: $CH_3CH_2CH(CH_3)CH_3$.

# ALKANES

## PHYSICAL PROPERTIES

> **Hydrocarbons** are molecules that contain **hydrogen** and **carbon ONLY**.

Alkanes are a **homologous series** of **saturated hydrocarbons**.

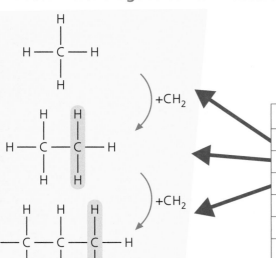

+CH$_2$

+CH$_2$

> See page 91 for rules about **names**.

| Name | Formula | Boiling point / °C |
|------|---------|-------------------|
| methane | CH$_4$ | −164 |
| ethane | C$_2$H$_6$ | −89 |
| propane | C$_3$H$_8$ | −42 |
| butane | C$_4$H$_{10}$ | −1 |
| pentane | C$_5$H$_{12}$ | 36 |
| hexane | C$_6$H$_{14}$ | 69 |

**boiling point increases**

> Alkanes are saturated because they contain **all single bonds**.

> Each straight chain alkane has an **'extra' CH$_2$**.

---

### KEY POINTS ABOUT HOMOLOGOUS SERIES

- Each molecular formula in the series has an extra 'CH$_2$'.
- Every homologous series has a general formula:

  e.g. **Alkanes: C$_n$H$_{(2n+2)}$**

  So, an alkane with 100 C atoms has the formula . . .

  C$_{100}$H$_{([2 \times 100] + 2)}$ = C$_{100}$H$_{202}$

- The compounds show a trend in physical properties.
- Boiling points increase down the group.
- Other homologous series include:
  - alcohols (page 123)
  - alkenes (page 107).

> **MUST CHECK**
>
> 'Polar covalent bonds' on page 27; 'Intermolecular forces' on page 29

---

**Why do boiling points increase down the series?**

bigger electron cloud

- The bonds in alkanes are non-polar as C and H have similar electronegativities.
- Therefore the molecules are non-polar.
- The intermolecular forces are induced dipole–induced dipole forces (often called van der Waals forces).
- The forces are stronger when the molecules become larger (down the series) because there is:
  - a bigger electron cloud that can be
  - more easily distorted
  - to form δ+ and δ− charges.

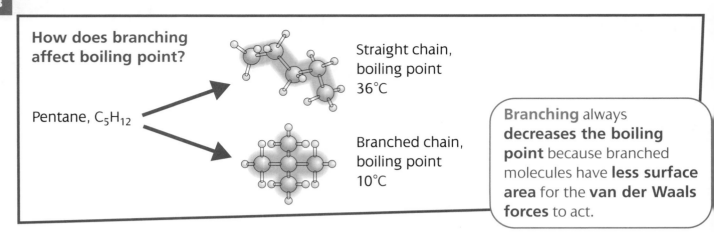

How does branching affect boiling point?

Pentane, $C_5H_{12}$

Straight chain, boiling point 36°C

Branched chain, boiling point 10°C

**Branching** always **decreases the boiling point** because branched molecules have **less surface area** for the **van der Waals forces** to act.

## REACTIONS OF ALKANES

Alkanes are unreactive because:

- The C–C and C–H bonds are strong – not easily broken.
- The bonds are non-polar so do not react with polar molecules or ions – e.g. water, acids and metals.

... BUT ...

All alkanes are used as fuels. They burn in air to give:

- carbon dioxide and water – complete combustion
- carbon monoxide and carbon if combustion is incomplete.

### COMBUSTION OF ALKANES

**Complete combustion** products are $CO_2$ and $H_2O$.

methane
$$CH_4(g) + 2O_2(g) \rightarrow CO_2(g) + 2H_2O(l) \qquad \Delta H_c^{\ominus} = -890 \text{ kJ mol}^{-1}$$

butane
$$C_4H_{10}(g) + 6\tfrac{1}{2}O_2(g) \rightarrow 4CO_2(g) + 5H_2O(l) \qquad \Delta H_c^{\ominus} = -2877 \text{ kJ mol}^{-1}$$

$\Delta H_c^{\ominus}$, **the enthalpy change of combustion**, is for **one mole of alkane** burned (see page 52).

All combustion reactions are **exothermic** ($\Delta H_c^{\ominus}$ is **negative**). **Bigger molecules** give out **more energy**.

## ENTHALPY CALCULATIONS

### WORKED EXAMPLE

Write the equation to show the enthalpy change of combustion of ethane. ($\Delta H_c^{\ominus} = -1560 \text{ kJ mol}^{-1}$)
Calculate the enthalpy change when 1.5 g ethane burns completely in air.

$$C_2H_6(g) + 3\tfrac{1}{2}O_2(g) \rightarrow 2CO_2(g) + 3H_2O(l) \qquad \Delta H_c^{\ominus} = -1560 \text{ kJ mol}^{-1}$$

Write $\Delta H_c^{\ominus}$ equation for **one molecule** of alkane.

Number of moles of ethane $= \dfrac{\text{mass}}{\text{molar mass}} = \dfrac{1.5}{30} = 0.05$ moles

$\Delta H_c^{\ominus}$ is **per mole** so work out **how many moles** of ethane burn ...

Enthalpy change $= 0.05 \times (-1560) = -78 \text{ kJ}$

... then **multiply** by $\Delta H_c^{\ominus}$ to get the **enthalpy change in kJ**.

# FOSSIL FUELS

## HOW ARE FOSSIL FUELS USED?

- **Coal** mainly carbon, burned in power stations to produce electricity
- **Gas** mainly methane (an alkane) used for heating homes
- **Oil** a mixture of hydrocarbons (mainly alkanes) separated by **fractional distillation**

Fossil fuels are useful fuels because:
- They are available in large quantities.
- Combustion in air is very exothermic – large energy output.
- Waste products are mainly gases – little solid waste.

## FRACTIONAL DISTILLATION OF CRUDE OIL

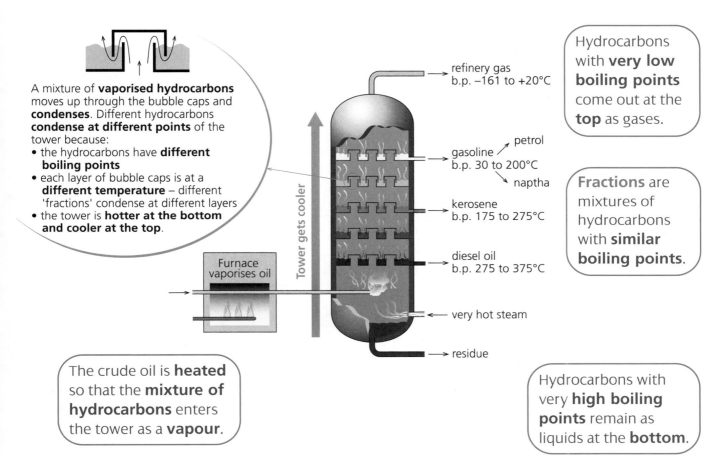

A mixture of **vaporised hydrocarbons** moves up through the bubble caps and **condenses**. Different hydrocarbons **condense at different points** of the tower because:
- the hydrocarbons have **different boiling points**
- each layer of bubble caps is at a **different temperature** – different 'fractions' condense at different layers
- the tower is **hotter at the bottom and cooler at the top**.

Furnace vaporises oil

Tower gets cooler

refinery gas b.p. −161 to +20°C

gasoline b.p. 30 to 200°C — petrol, naptha

kerosene b.p. 175 to 275°C

diesel oil b.p. 275 to 375°C

very hot steam

residue

Hydrocarbons with **very low boiling points** come out at the **top** as gases.

**Fractions** are mixtures of hydrocarbons with **similar boiling points**.

The crude oil is **heated** so that the **mixture of hydrocarbons** enters the tower as a **vapour**.

Hydrocarbons with very **high boiling points** remain as liquids at the **bottom**.

## FUEL CONSERVATION

**Why conserve fossil fuels?**
- They are **non-renewable** or finite – will run out.
- Oil is needed to make chemicals – plastics, fibres, medicines, etc.
- Waste gases from combustion are polluting – see following page.

**What can be done?**
- Reduce total fuel consumption by using fuels more efficiently.
- Use **renewable** fuels where possible. For example:
  – biofuels (e.g. wood, biogas) – if replanted these do not increase the carbon content of the atmosphere
  – alternate energy resources e.g. wind, solar.
- Remove pollutants from waste gases – see following page.

# AIR POLLUTION FROM FOSSIL FUELS

**Carbon dioxide $CO_2$**
- is formed when **fuels burn**
- **absorbs infra-red radiation** (heat) from the Earth:
  - this **warms the atmosphere** and adds to the **greenhouse effect**
  - this may cause **long-term climate change**, e.g. polar ice caps melt, sea levels rise, climate changes drastically.

**Carbon monoxide CO**
- is formed by **incomplete combustion** due to **limited oxygen availability**
- is **toxic** to humans because it **blocks oxygen transport** in the blood.

**Unburned hydrocarbons $C_xH_y$**
- come from **fuel leaks** or **unburned fuel** escaping from exhausts
- are **greenhouse gases**, form **smog** and can cause **cancer**.

**Nitrogen oxides $NO_x$**
- are formed when **nitrogen** (in air) **reacts with oxygen** due to the **high temperatures** and **electrical discharges** in a car engine
- cause **acid rain** and **smog**
- can cause **cancer** and **breathing problems**.

**Sulphur dioxide $SO_2$**
- is formed when **sulphur impurities** in the fuel **burn**
- dissolve in rain water to form **acid rain**:

$$SO_2 + H_2O \rightarrow H_2SO_3 \xrightarrow{\text{oxidation}} \underset{\text{sulphuric acid}}{H_2SO_4}$$

  - acid rain **kills trees**, **harms crops** and **harms or kills** living things in **lakes**.

## REMOVING POLLUTANTS FROM WASTE GASES

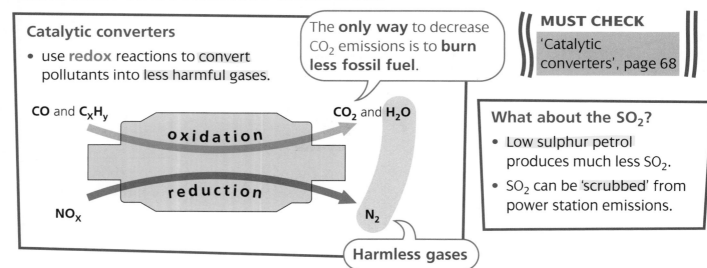

**Catalytic converters**
- use **redox** reactions to **convert** pollutants into less harmful gases.

The **only way** to decrease $CO_2$ emissions is to **burn less fossil fuel**.

**MUST CHECK**
'Catalytic converters', page 68

CO and $C_xH_y$ → **oxidation** → $CO_2$ and $H_2O$

$NO_x$ → **reduction** → $N_2$

Harmless gases

**What about the $SO_2$?**
- Low sulphur petrol produces much less $SO_2$.
- $SO_2$ can be 'scrubbed' from power station emissions.

---

**WORKED EXAMPLE**

Benzene, $C_6H_6$, is a component of petrol and is linked to some cancers.

(a) Explain why benzene is present in car engine exhaust gases.
(b) Explain, with the help of an equation, how it is removed.

(a) Benzene is a hydrocarbon. Some hydrocarbons pass through the **engine without being burned** and so are present in the exhaust gases.
(b) Benzene is removed by being **oxidised** by reactions in the **catalytic converter** to form carbon dioxide and water.
$$C_6H_6 + 7\tfrac{1}{2}O_2 \rightarrow 6CO_2 + 3H_2O$$
Same equation as **combustion**!

# CRACKING

## WHAT IS CRACKING?

**Crude oil** ... is separated by **fractional distillation** to give ... **Oil fractions**

Petrol is in very high demand.

**Oil fractions**
Gases ($C_1$–$C_4$)
Petrol/naphtha ($C_5$–$C_{14}$)
Kerosene ($C_9$–$C_{16}$)
Diesel oil ($C_{15}$–$C_{25}$)
Lubricating oil ($C_{20}$–$C_{70}$)
Residue (>$C_{70}$)

longer chain length

**Cracking** splits longer chain molecules into more useful shorter chain molecules.

Longer chain fractions are less useful.

**Thermal cracking** uses heat to split molecules.

**Catalytic cracking** uses a catalyst to split molecules.

## THERMAL CRACKING

| Conditions | Feedstock is mixed with steam in a cracking furnace at 900°C |
|---|---|
| Feedstock | Naphtha/kerosene |
| Products | Small molecules $C_2$–$C_5$ alkenes and alkanes |
| Uses of products | Making polymers |

**No catalyst** is used, but the temperature is **very high** – expensive!

**Feedstock** is the **mixture of reactants** used.

Cracking is not just used for making petrol – **thermal cracking** makes alkenes for **polymerisation** (see page 113).

## HOMOLYTIC BOND FISSION

**Homolytic** means **one electron** goes to each part-molecule – **free radical**.

**Homolytic** **bond fission**

bond fission = breaking bonds

**2 shared electrons** in a single covalent bond

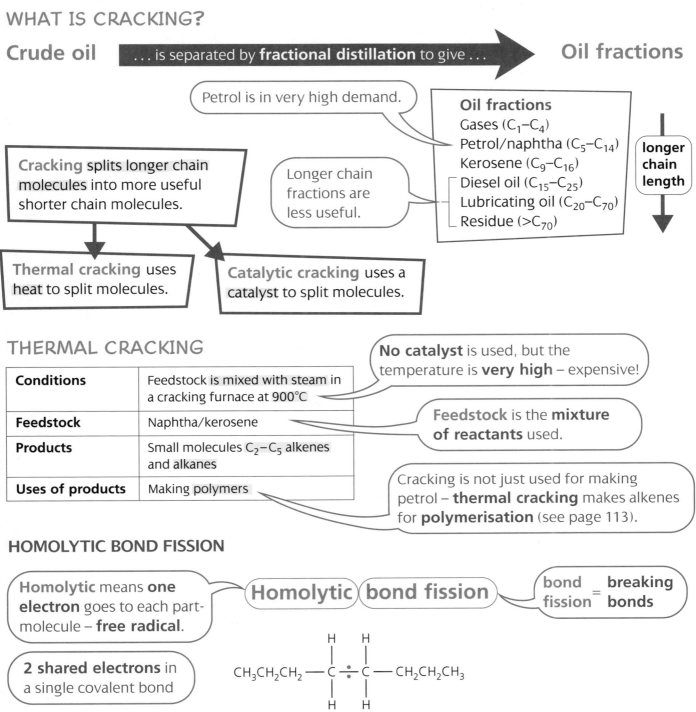

heat and high pressure

**1 electron** goes to each part-molecule – **homolytic fission**.

A molecule with a single, **unpaired electron** is called a **free radical**. **Remember** 'homo' means 'same'.

Further reactions form the products:

$CH_3CH_2CH=CH_2$      $CH_3CH_2CH_2CH_3$

# CATALYTIC CRACKING

| Conditions | Zeolite catalyst 500°C |
|---|---|
| Feedstock | Gas oil (diesel oil) |
| Products | Smaller molecules: alkenes, branched and cyclic molecules |
| Uses of products | Added to petrol to improve efficiency of combustion |

**Zeolites** are used in cracking hydrocarbon molecules. These are catalyst molecules with holes or **'pores'**. The gas oil molecules **fit inside** and are cracked.

A **lower temperature** is used but the feedstock is left in the reactor longer than for thermal cracking.

The **structure** of the molecules **changes**.

## HETEROLYTIC BOND FISSION

**Heterolytic** means **both electrons** go to one part-molecule – making two **ions**.

Heterolytic bond fission

$\dfrac{\text{bond}}{\text{fission}} = \dfrac{\text{breaking}}{\text{bonds}}$

$$CH_3CH_2CH_2 - \overset{\overset{\displaystyle H}{|}}{C} \vdots \overset{\overset{\displaystyle H}{|}}{\underset{\underset{\displaystyle H}{|}}{C}} - CH_2CH_2CH_3$$

**2 shared electrons** in a single covalent bond

zeolite catalyst

**BOTH** electrons go to one part-molecule.

One part-molecule has a **positive charge**:
**carbocation**

containing **positive**
**carbon** ion

$$CH_3CH_2CH_2 - \overset{\overset{\displaystyle H}{|}}{\underset{\underset{\displaystyle H}{|}}{C^{\oplus}}} \qquad \overset{\ominus}{\phantom{.}}\overset{\overset{\displaystyle H}{|}}{\underset{\underset{\displaystyle H}{|}}{C}} - CH_2CH_2CH_3$$

The part-molecule that 'keeps' the electrons has a **negative charge**.

The **carbocation** reacts with other molecules in mixture to form branched chain molecules – these are very important in increasing fuel efficiency in petrol.

### WORKED EXAMPLE

Write three different equations for the cracking of heptane to produce two product molecules.
Write your equations using condensed structural formulae.
(Heptane: CH₃CH₂CH₂CH₂CH₂CH₂CH₃)

Hint – there are **3 places** heptane can 'crack'.

$$CH_3CH_2CH_2CH_2CH_2CH_2CH_3$$

... or the same at the other end!

$CH_3CH_2CH_2CH_2CH_2CH_2CH_3 \rightarrow CH_4 + CH_2{=}CHCH_2CH_2CH_2CH_3$

$CH_3CH_2CH_2CH_2CH_2CH_2CH_3 \rightarrow CH_3CH_3 + CH_2{=}CHCH_2CH_2CH_3$

$CH_3CH_2CH_2CH_2CH_2CH_2CH_3 \rightarrow CH_3CH_2CH_3 + CH_2{=}CHCH_2CH_3$

Work out the **numbers of Cs** in the formula first, and then work out **Hs** by making the molecule into an **alkane** ($C_nH_{(2n+2)}$) or **alkene** ($C_nH_{(2n)}$).

There are more possibilities – the **double bond** could go into either compound.

Any straight chain molecule has enough hydrogens to form **ONE ALKANE** and **ONE ALKENE** – this works **every time**!

# ISOMERISM AND REFORMING

## BETTER PETROL

It is important to improve the **efficiency of combustion** of petrol because:

- **less fuel** needs to be burned
- which **saves finite crude oil** reserves
- and is **less environmentally harmful**
- and **costs less money** to the motorist.

Petrol burns more efficiently when it contains more . . .

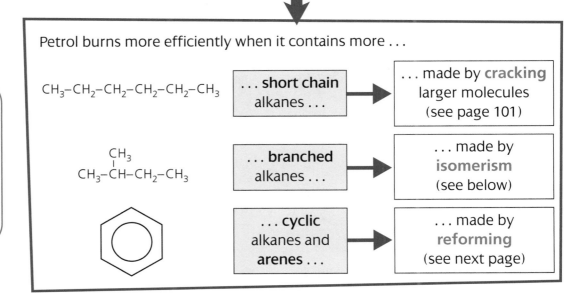

$CH_3-CH_2-CH_2-CH_2-CH_2-CH_3$ → . . . **short chain** alkanes . . . → . . . made by **cracking** larger molecules (see page 101)

$CH_3-CH-CH_2-CH_3$ with $CH_3$ branch → . . . **branched** alkanes . . . → . . . made by **isomerism** (see below)

→ . . . **cyclic** alkanes and arenes . . . → . . . made by **reforming** (see next page)

Adding these molecules to petrol increases the **octane rating** – this indicates how efficiently the fuel burns.

**MUST CHECK**
'Isomers', page 95

## ISOMERISM

| Conditions | Catalyst (Pt/AlO$_3$) Heat (150°C) |
|---|---|
| Feedstock | C$_4$–C$_6$ alkenes |
| Products | Branched alkanes with same molecular formulae |
| Uses of products | Added to petrol to improve efficiency of combustion |

**KEY POINTS**

- **Isomerism** does not change the molecular formula – the same numbers of atoms are in the molecule.
- Isomerism changes straight chain molecules into branched molecules.

## For example

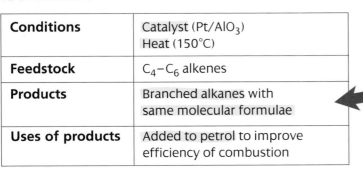

$CH_3-CH_2-CH_2-CH_2-CH_3$ —isomerism→ $CH_3-CH-CH_2-CH_3$ with $CH_3$ branch

pentane → 2-methylbutane

Both molecules have the **same molecular formula** – $C_5H_{12}$

2-methylbutane is an **isomer** of pentane.

Branched molecules increase the **efficiency of combustion** of petrol.

## WORKED EXAMPLE

Pentane, $C_5H_{12}$, can be isomerised to give two branched isomers.
Give the names and structures of the two isomers.

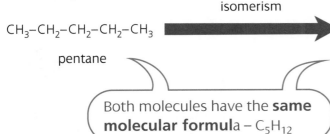

2-methylbutane $CH_3 — CH — CH_2 — CH_3$ with $CH_3$ branch

2,2-dimethylpropane

# REFORMING

| Conditions | Catalyst ($Pt/AlO_3$)<br>Heat (500°C) |
|---|---|
| Feedstock | Naptha ($C_6-C_{10}$) |
| Products | Cyclic molecules with same number of carbons |
| Uses of products | Added to petrol to improve efficiency of combustion |

> **KEY POINTS**
> - **Reformed** molecules have the same number of C atoms but contain fewer H atoms.
> - **Cyclic** molecules contain rings of C atoms.

## CYCLIC ALKANES

**Cyclic alkanes** contain rings of carbon atoms with all single bonds.

**For example**

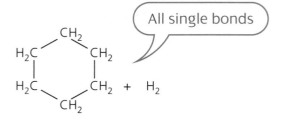

All single bonds

$$CH_3-CH_2-CH_2-CH_2-CH_2-CH_3 \xrightarrow{\text{reforming}}$$

hexane, $C_6H_{14}$

cyclohexane, $C_6H_{12}$ + $H_2$

Both contain 6 carbon atoms ...

... but $C_6H_{12}$ contains fewer H atoms.

## ARENES

**Arenes** (sometimes called 'aromatics') contain **benzene rings** – these have even fewer hydrogen atoms.

**For example**

$$CH_3-CH_2-CH_2-CH_2-CH_2-CH_3 \dashrightarrow$$  + 4$H_2$

hexane, $C_6H_{14}$

benzene $C_6H_6$

Both contain **6 carbon atoms**.

Reforming to give arenes involves **several reaction stages**.

---

### WORKED EXAMPLE

The following three equations show reactions that are used to produce molecules for adding to petrol.
Name the type of reaction occurring in each equation and explain your reasoning.

1. $CH_3CH_2CH_2CH_2CH_2CH_2CH_3 \rightarrow CH_3CH_2CH_3 + CH_2=CHCH_2CH_3$

2. $CH_3CH_2CH_2CH_2CH_2CH_2CH_3 \rightarrow$ 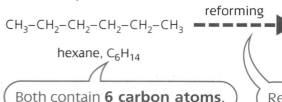 $+ 4H_2$

3. $CH_3CH_2CH_2CH_2CH_2CH_3 \rightarrow CH_3CH(CH_3)CH_2CH_2CH_3$

1. This is a **cracking** reaction. A larger molecule has been split to form **two molecules**, one of which has a **double bond**.

2. This is a **reforming** reaction. A **cyclic molecule** with the **same number of carbon atoms**, but **fewer hydrogen** atoms has been formed.

3. This is an **isomerism** reaction. A **branched molecule** with the **same molecular formula** has been formed.

# REACTIONS OF ALKANES WITH HALOGENS

## HALOGENOALKANES

**Halogenoalkanes** form when one or more hydrogen atoms in an alkane are **substituted** for halogen atoms.

**For example**

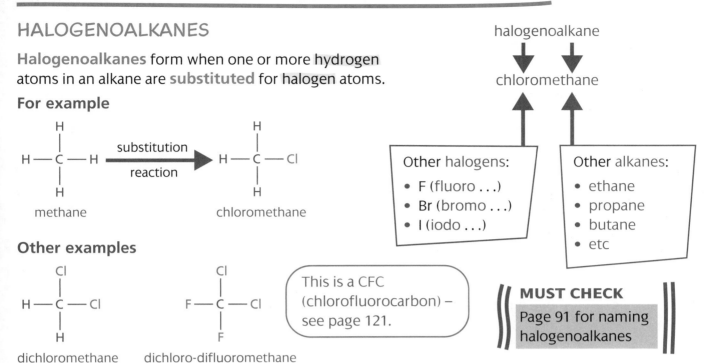

methane    →    chloromethane

substitution reaction

**Other examples**

dichloromethane    dichloro-difluoromethane

This is a CFC (chlorofluorocarbon) – see page 121.

halogenoalkane

chloromethane

Other halogens:
- F (fluoro ...)
- Br (bromo ...)
- I (iodo ...)

Other alkanes:
- ethane
- propane
- butane
- etc

**MUST CHECK**

Page 91 for naming halogenoalkanes

## MECHANISM OF CHLORINATION OF METHANE

The mechanism of reacting chlorine with methane involves ...

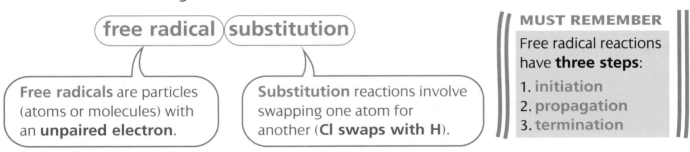

**free radical**   **substitution**

**Free radicals** are particles (atoms or molecules) with an **unpaired electron**.

**Substitution** reactions involve swapping one atom for another (**Cl swaps with H**).

**MUST REMEMBER**

Free radical reactions have **three steps**:
1. **initiation**
2. **propagation**
3. **termination**

### INITIATION

**Initiation** starts the reaction by producing **new free radicals** by **homolytic fission**.

Homolytic fission uses light energy (UV light) to split a chlorine molecule into two free radicals.

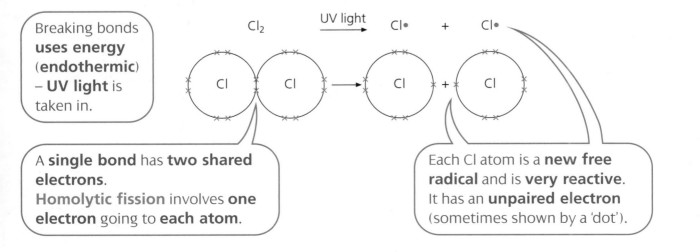

$Cl_2$   —UV light→   $Cl\bullet$   +   $Cl\bullet$

Breaking bonds **uses energy (endothermic)** – **UV light** is taken in.

A **single bond** has **two shared electrons**.
**Homolytic fission** involves **one electron** going to **each atom**.

Each Cl atom is a **new free radical** and is **very reactive**. It has an **unpaired electron** (sometimes shown by a 'dot').

## PROPAGATION

Propagation continues the reaction. **Free radicals** react with **molecules** and a **new free radical** is always made.

1. Chlorine free radicals react with methane molecules.

$$Cl\cdot + CH_4 \rightarrow CH_3\cdot + HCl$$

A **new free radical** is always made so the reaction can continue to **propagate**.

2. Any free radical can react with any molecule in the reaction mixture. These reactions also happen during propagation.

$$CH_3\cdot + Cl_2 \rightarrow CH_3Cl + Cl\cdot$$
$$CH_3Cl + Cl\cdot \rightarrow CH_2Cl\cdot + HCl$$
$$CH_2Cl\cdot + Cl_2 \rightarrow CH_2Cl_2 + Cl\cdot$$

Cl· radicals can remove **more H atoms** so the products contain . . .

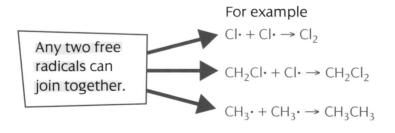

| $CH_3Cl$ | $CH_2Cl_2$ | $CHCl_3$ | $CCl_4$ |

**more chlorine** present, **longer** contact **time**

## TERMINATION

Termination ends the reaction by **removing free radicals** from the reaction mixture – **two free radicals react together** to form a molecule.

Any two free radicals can join together.

For example
$$Cl\cdot + Cl\cdot \rightarrow Cl_2$$

$$CH_2Cl\cdot + Cl\cdot \rightarrow CH_2Cl_2$$

$$CH_3\cdot + CH_3\cdot \rightarrow CH_3CH_3$$

Notice that **no free radicals are made** – the reaction is finished.

There are lots of **other possibilities** – the final product is a **mixture of different molecules**.

## WORKED EXAMPLE

Chlorine reacts with ethane to produce chloroethane, $C_2H_5Cl$.
Describe the mechanism for this reaction.

The reaction is a free radical substitution reaction.
Initiation: Chlorine splits by homolytic fission using UV light.

$$Cl_2 \rightarrow Cl\cdot + Cl\cdot$$

Propagation: The Cl· radical removes a hydrogen atom from ethane.

$$Cl\cdot + C_2H_6 \rightarrow C_2H_5\cdot + HCl$$

Termination: Two radicals join to form a molecule.

$$Cl\cdot + C_2H_5\cdot \rightarrow C_2H_5Cl$$

'Describe' means 'use words and equations'. Be sure to mention the 'key words' like:
- **free radical substitution**
- **homolytic fission**
- **initiation**
- **propagation**
- **termination**.

The question asks how **$C_2H_5Cl$ is formed** – no need to go into equations for other reactions.

# ALKENES: STRUCTURE AND BONDING

## WHAT IS AN ALKENE?

- **Alkenes** are **hydrocarbons** that contain a **double bond**.
- They contain **hydrogen** and **carbon only**.

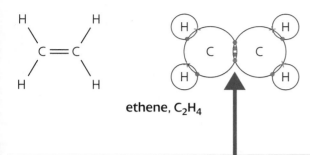

ethene, $C_2H_4$

The double bond is formed by **4 shared electrons**. Therefore:

- Alkenes are **unsaturated** – they can 'add on' more atoms in **addition reactions** (see page 109).
- The double bond is an area of **high electron density**.

The double bond forms when the 2s and 2p atomic orbitals of C atoms overlap.

This forms one σ molecular bond and one π molecular bond.

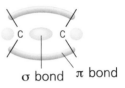

σ bond    π bond

## HOMOLOGOUS SERIES

| Name | Formula | |
|------|---------|---|
| ethene | $C_2H_4$ | 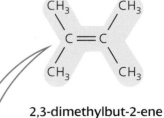 |
| propene | $C_3H_6$ | |
| butene | $C_4H_8$ | |

$+CH_2$

$+CH_2$

The alkenes are a **homologous series** because:

- Each molecular formula in the series has an extra '$CH_2$'.
- They have the general formula:
  $$C_nH_{(2n)}$$
- They show a **trend in physical properties**.
- **Boiling points increase** down the series.

## MORE ALKENES

**MUST CHECK**

Page 91 for more help with naming compounds.

Alkenes can have **straight chains** . . .

. . . or **branched chains**.

but-2-ene

2,3-dimethylbut-2-ene

The number gives the **position** of the **double bond**.

The C=C double bond is usually **drawn horizontally** in the molecule like this.

# SHAPES OF ALKENE MOLECULES

Carbon atoms with a **double bond** are surrounded by 3 groups of electrons.
The three bonds form a **flat plane** with a **bond angle of 120°**.

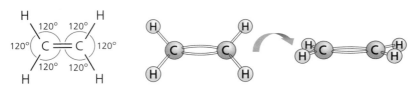

This shape is called **trigonal planar**.

The molecule is **flat**.

## Shapes of other alkenes

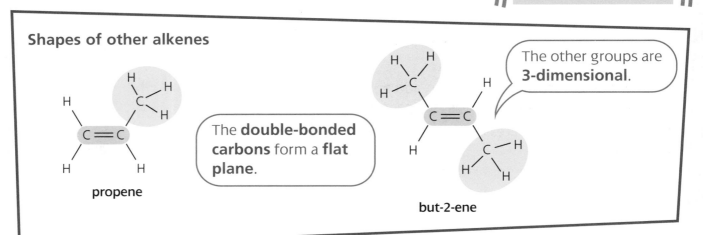

The **double-bonded carbons** form a **flat plane**.

The other groups are **3-dimensional**.

propene

but-2-ene

# ISOMERS OF ALKENES

Larger alkenes can have the double bond in **different positions**.

$CH_2=CHCH_2CH_2CH_3$

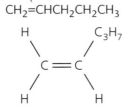

pent-1-ene

$CH_3CH=CHCH_2CH_3$

cis-pent-2-ene

$CH_3CH=CHCH_2CH_3$

trans-pent-2-ene

There is **no free rotation** about the double bond so larger alkenes have *cis* and *trans* **isomers**.

## WORKED EXAMPLE

Name the following alkene molecules

hex-1-ene

3-ethyl-2-methylpent-2-ene

1. Use the **longest chain** to name the alkene (e.g. $C_5$ = pentene).
2. Give the **position** of the double bond (e.g. -2-).
3. Name and give the position of any **branches** (e.g. 3-ethyl).

# REACTIONS OF ALKENES

## ALKENES AND BROMINE

Aqueous bromine – often called bromine water – is used to test for a double bond.

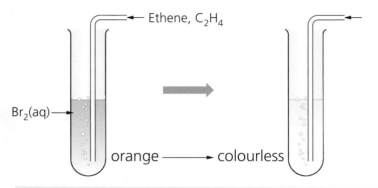

Br$_2$(aq)⟶  orange ⟶ colourless

A double bond **decolourises** bromine water.

ethene                          1,2-dibromoethane

$$C_2H_4 \ + \ Br_2 \ \rightarrow \ C_2H_4Br_2$$

Name now ends in **-ane** because it contains all **single bonds** – it is **saturated**.

Each **alkene** contains a **double bond** – it is **unsaturated**.

propene                          1,2-dibromopropane

**MUST REMEMBER**

These are **addition reactions** – bromine atoms are **added** to the molecule across the **double bond**.

---

**WORKED EXAMPLE**

The equations show the reactions of ethane and ethene with bromine.

ethane
Equation 1: $CH_3CH_3 + Br_2 \rightarrow CH_3CH_2Br + HBr$

ethene
Equation 2: $CH_2{=}CH_2 + Br_2 \rightarrow CH_2BrCH_2Br$

(a) Which compound in the equations is unsaturated? Explain your reasoning.

(b) Use information from the equations to discuss the difference between addition and substitution reactions.

(a) Ethene is **unsaturated** because it contains a **double bond**.

(b) Equation 1 shows a **substitution reaction** because a hydrogen atom has been substituted (changed) for a bromine atom in the ethane molecule.
Equation 2 shows an **addition reaction** because bromine has been added to the ethene molecule across the double bond. The product molecule is now saturated.

**MUST CHECK**

The **differences** between **addition** and **substitution** reactions – see page 105.

# MORE ADDITION REACTIONS

## HYDROGENATION (+ $H_2$)

The groups attached to the C atom could be:

- H atoms
- alkyl groups (straight or branched) e.g. methyl, $CH_3$, or ethyl, $C_2H_5$.

The reaction uses a **nickel catalyst**.

$$\underset{/}{\overset{\backslash}{C}} = \underset{\backslash}{\overset{/}{C}} \quad + \quad H_2 \quad \xrightarrow[\text{catalyst}]{\text{Ni}} \quad -\underset{|}{\overset{|}{C}} - \underset{|}{\overset{|}{C}} - \\ \qquad\qquad\qquad\qquad\qquad\qquad H \quad H$$

Another **addition reaction** – H atoms have been added to the molecule.

### Vegetable oils

- Vegetable oils are usually liquids.
- They contain long chain molecules with **many double bonds – polyunsaturated**.
- This reaction is used to **hydrogenate** some of the double bonds.
- Hydrogenated vegetable oils are solids so can be used in margarines.

## HYDROGEN HALIDES (+ HX)

hydrogen halide                    halogenoalkane

**X** = any **halogen** e.g. **Cl**, **Br**

$$\underset{/}{\overset{\backslash}{C}} = \underset{\backslash}{\overset{/}{C}} \quad + \quad HX \quad \longrightarrow \quad -\underset{|}{\overset{|}{C}} - \underset{|}{\overset{|}{C}} - \\ \qquad\qquad\qquad\qquad\qquad\qquad H \quad X$$

In **addition** reactions only **one product molecule** is formed.

**For example**

propene       hydrogen bromide

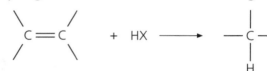

$$\underset{H}{\overset{H}{\underset{\backslash}{C}}} = \underset{H}{\overset{CH_3}{\underset{/}{C}}} \quad + \quad HBr \quad \longrightarrow \quad H - \underset{H}{\overset{H}{\underset{|}{C}}} - \underset{Br}{\overset{H}{\underset{|}{C}}} - CH_3$$

## REACTION WITH STEAM TO MAKE ALCOHOLS (+ $H_2O$)

ethene              steam                  ethanol

$$\underset{H}{\overset{H}{\underset{\backslash}{C}}} = \underset{H}{\overset{H}{\underset{/}{C}}} \quad + \quad H_2O \quad \xrightarrow[\substack{H_3PO_4 \\ \text{catalyst}}]{\substack{70 \text{ atm} \\ 300°C}} \quad H - \underset{H}{\overset{H}{\underset{|}{C}}} - \underset{H}{\overset{H}{\underset{|}{C}}} - OH$$

### Conditions

- High temperature
- Acid catalyst ($H^+$)

- This reaction converts ethene (from cracking crude oil fractions) to ethanol.
- Ethanol is a very important solvent in industry, e.g. making perfumes, cosmetics and dyes.

### KEY POINTS

- **Alkenes** react by addition because they are unsaturated – contain a double bond.
- Reacting molecules are added across the double bond.
- Product molecules are saturated – contain all single bonds.

# ADDITION REACTION MECHANISMS

Edexcel: **detailed** mechanism not required

## REACTION OF BROMINE WITH ALKENES

The **reaction mechanism** has three steps:

---

**Step 1** The C=C double bond induces a dipole in the $Br_2$ molecule.

Remember the C=C double bond is an area of **high electron density**.

$$C=C$$
$$Br^{\delta+}$$
$$Br^{\delta-}$$

The double bond **repels** (pushes away) the electron cloud around the $Br_2$ molecule, giving it a $\delta+$ and $\delta-$ **dipole**.

---

**Step 2** The $Br_2$ reacts with the double bond.

**Curly arrows** show the movement of a pair of electrons:

- One pair of electrons in the C=C double bond makes a single bond with one Br atom.

- The pair of electrons in the Br–Br bond goes to the other Br atom (forming $Br^-$).

$$C=C \quad Br^{\delta+} \quad Br^{\delta-} \quad \rightarrow \quad -\overset{|}{C}-\overset{|}{C^+}- \quad Br \quad :\!\overset{..}{\underset{..}{Br}}\!:^-$$

An **intermediate positive carbocation** and a **bromide ion** are formed.

The Br–Br bond breaks by **heterolytic fission – both** electrons go to one **Br atom**.

$Br_2$ acts as an **electrophile** i.e. an electron pair acceptor.

---

**Step 3** The $Br^-$ ion adds on to the positive ion.

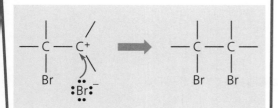

A **single bond** is formed by a **lone pair of electrons** on the $Br^-$ ion.

---

## WHAT IS AN ELECTROPHILE?

**Definition: an electrophile is an electron pair acceptor.**

The reaction mechanism for reactions of alkenes is **electrophilic addition**.

**Key points**

Electrophiles:

- are attracted to areas of negative charge (high electron density) in molecules
- are formed by **heterolytic fission** – both electrons in a bond go to one atom
- accept pairs of electrons e.g. from double bonds or lone pairs.

---

### WORKED EXAMPLE

(a) Explain why bromine is considered to be an electrophile in the addition of bromine to ethene.

(b) The bromine molecule splits by heterolytic fission. Explain what this means.

(a) Because it **accepts a pair of electrons** from the C=C double bond.

(b) Both electrons go to one atom, to give a $Br^-$ ion.

# PREDICTING PRODUCTS FOR UNSYMMETRICAL ALKENES

Propene is **unsymmetrical** – the double bond is **not in the middle**.

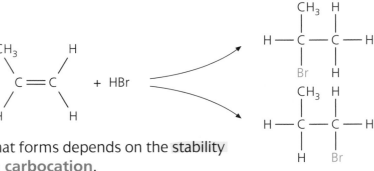

There are 2 possible products.

- The major product that forms depends on the **stability** of the **intermediate carbocation**.
- The rule is: **An electrophile adds to an unsymmetrical** alkene so that the **most stable carbocation** forms as an intermediate.

## WHICH IS THE MOST STABLE CARBOCATION?

The more C atoms joined to the $C^+$ atom, the more stable the carbocation.

**R** is an **alkyl** group, for example:
- $CH_3$
- $C_2H_5$

| Primary carbocation | Secondary carbocation | Tertiary carbocation |
|---|---|---|
| R<br>\ <br>$C^+$—H<br>/ <br>H | R<br>\ <br>$C^+$—H<br>/ <br>R | R<br>\ <br>$C^+$—R<br>/ <br>R |
| The $C^+$ atom is joined to one other C atom. | The $C^+$ atom is joined to two other C atoms. | The $C^+$ atom is joined to three other C atoms. |

**MORE STABLE** →

## HYDROGEN BROMIDE AND PROPENE

**Primary carbocation:** $C^+$ is joined to **1** other C atom.

Note: HBr has a **permanent dipole**.

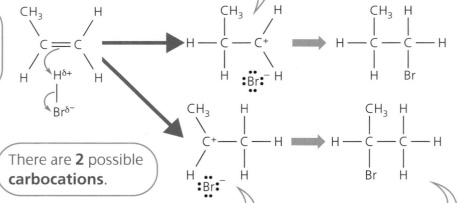

There are **2 possible carbocations**.

**Secondary carbocation:** $C^+$ is joined to **2** other C atoms. → **Most likely ('major') product**.

---

## WORKED EXAMPLE

The following carbocations form as intermediates in the hydration of propene to propanol.

Ⓐ   H   CH₃
     \   /
   $C^+$—C—H
     /   |
    H    H

Ⓑ   H   CH₃
     |   /
 H—C—$C^+$
     |   \
     H    H

(a) Which is the most stable carbocation? Explain your reasoning.
(b) What is the formula of the major product of the reaction?

(a) The most stable carbocation is B because the $C^+$ atom is joined to two other C atoms rather than only one (as in A).
(b) Structure of product:

In the last step of hydration, **OH⁻** adds on to the carbocation.

    H    CH₃
    |    |
 H—C—C—OH
    |    |
    H    H

# ADDITION POLYMERISATION

## POLYMERS FROM ALKENES

**Alkenes** polymerise by **addition** – the double bonds open and the molecules join together in long chains. No other products are formed.

**For example**

ethene monomer → repeating unit of poly(ethene)

**Ethene:**
- is a **monomer** – **single molecule** ...
- with a **double bond**.

Many monomers join.

Polymers contain many repeating units.

**Poly(ethene)** is used for **plastic packaging**, e.g. bottles, carrier bags, food bags.

**Poly(ethene):**
- is a **polymer** – **long chain** of repeating units ...
- with all **single bonds**.

## OTHER EXAMPLES

propene → poly(propene)

chloroethene → poly(chloroethene)

**Poly(propene)** is a **harder**, **stronger** plastic, e.g. used for bottle tops, plastic storage boxes.

**Poly(chloroethene) (PVC)** is **flexible**, e.g. used for wellies, guttering.

## STRUCTURES OF MONOMERS AND POLYMERS

Always draw **monomers** with a **double bond**.

monomer

repeating unit of polymer

## MUST REMEMBER
- Draw **polymers** as **repeating units** with **single bonds**.
- Put **square brackets** round the repeating units.
- Use '**n**' for 'many'.
- **Show bonds** coming out of brackets.

## WORKED EXAMPLE

(a) This is the structure of poly(phenylethene) – known as polystyrene.

Draw the structure of the phenylethene monomer.

(a)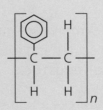

Exam questions often give the monomer and ask for the polymer or vice versa.

(b) This is the structure of a tetrafluoroethene monomer.

Draw the structure of the poly(tetrafluoroethene) polymer — known as Teflon.

(b)

# DISPOSAL OF WASTE POLYMERS

**Waste plastics** cause problems because:

- They are non-biodegradable – do not rot – so take up space permanently in landfill sites.
- Making new polymers uses up crude oil, which is finite – throwing away plastic is a waste of valuable hydrocarbons.
- Polymers can be burned – wasting plastic wastes energy.

**Biodegradable** plastics:

- **save long term space** in landfill

BUT:

- are **expensive** to develop
- are often **weaker** than non-biodegradable plastics
- do not reduce landfill space in the **short term**.

**Recycling** waste plastics:

- **saves** using **landfills** and **conserves** valuable oil **resources**.

BUT:

- **Collection**, **transport** and **sorting** can be **more expensive**, and use **more energy** than making new polymers from oil!

**Combustion** of waste plastics:

- can be used to **produce energy** for industry or electricity.

BUT:

- **Technology** needs to **develop further** to use plastics as fuels.
- **Harmful gases** are given off – power stations are already under pressure to reduce emissions.

**Hydrogen chloride**, **HCl**, is a toxic gas that comes from burning polymers containing chlorine.

**Make new chemicals** from waste plastics by:

1. converting waste **back to monomers** and then **repolymerising** them

2. **cracking** waste into smaller molecules and then **using as a feedstock**

- Both methods conserve crude oil resources and make new useful products.

BUT:

- **Collection**, **transport** and **sorting** can be **more expensive**, and use more energy, than making new polymers from oil!
- Large scale processes are **not yet fully developed**.

# ALKENES IN INDUSTRY

## REACTIONS OF ALKENES

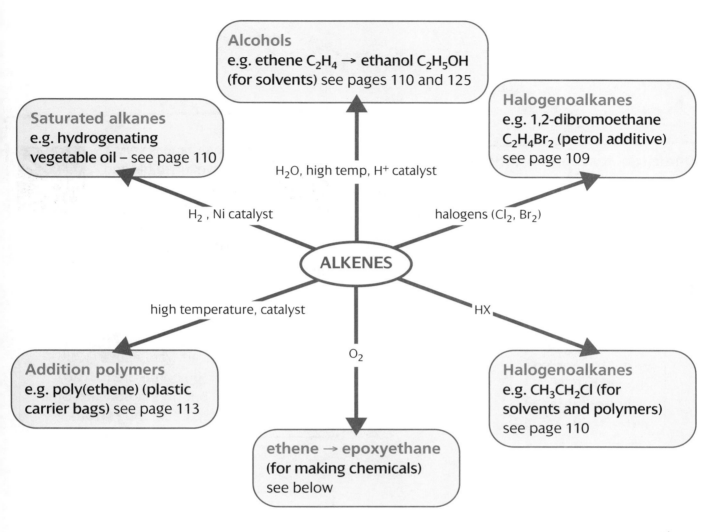

**Alcohols**
e.g. ethene $C_2H_4 \rightarrow$ ethanol $C_2H_5OH$
(for solvents) see pages 110 and 125

**Saturated alkanes**
e.g. hydrogenating
vegetable oil – see page 110

**Halogenoalkanes**
e.g. 1,2-dibromoethane
$C_2H_4Br_2$ (petrol additive)
see page 109

$H_2O$, high temp, $H^+$ catalyst

$H_2$, Ni catalyst

halogens ($Cl_2$, $Br_2$)

**ALKENES**

high temperature, catalyst

HX

$O_2$

**Addition polymers**
e.g. poly(ethene) (plastic
carrier bags) see page 113

**Halogenoalkanes**
e.g. $CH_3CH_2Cl$ (for
solvents and polymers)
see page 110

**ethene → epoxyethane**
(for making chemicals)
see below

## EPOXYETHANE

**Epoxyethane** is a very important synthetic reaction intermediate that is made from ethene.

Epoxyethane
**does not occur
naturally** – it is
made by chemical
synthesis.

**synthetic** **reaction intermediate**

All epoxyethane is
used in reactions
to form other
products – e.g.
solvents.

**Epoxyethane** is made by reacting ethene with oxygen:

$$C_2H_4 + \tfrac{1}{2}O_2 \rightarrow$$

It is:

- a very reactive reaction intermediate
- very hazardous as it is flammable and explosive
- used on a very large scale to make solvents for cosmetics,
  dyes and paints, and to make fibres e.g. polyesters.

# MANUFACTURE OF EPOXYETHANE

**Ethene** made by cracking alkanes from crude oil . . .

. . . is **oxidised** to form. . .

. . . **epoxyethane.**

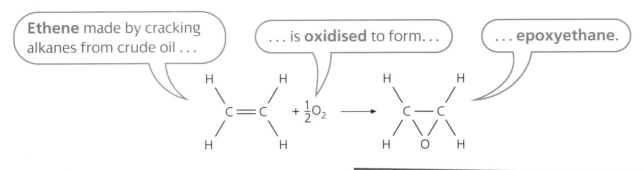

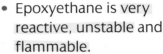

## Industrial reaction conditions

- Finely divided silver (Ag) catalyst
- 250 – 400°C
- 1000 – 3000 kPa pressure

## Hazards!

- Epoxyethane is very reactive, unstable and flammable.
- Very great care is taken during manufacture to avoid explosion.

## REACTIONS OF EPOXYETHANE

The 3-membered (3-atom) ring is **very strained** so epoxyethane is **very unstable** and **reactive**.

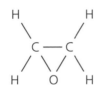

The **3-membered ring** is **strained** because:
- The **bond angles** are very **acute** (120°).
- The **electrons** in the bonds are **forced close together**, but they **repel** each other, pushing the ring apart creating **strain**.

## REACTION WITH WATER

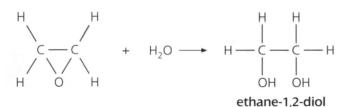

ethane-1,2-diol

## Reaction conditions

- 60°C
- Acid (H$^+$) catalyst

**Ethane-1,2-diol** is used to make antifreezes and polyesters.

## WORKED EXAMPLE

(a) Which of the following terms describes the reaction of epoxyethane with water?
   addition    dehydration    elimination    substitution
(b) Explain your reasoning.
(c) Epoxyethane is hazardous due to its flammability.
   Write an equation for the combustion of epoxyethane.

(a) Addition
(b) A water molecule adds on to the epoxyethane molecule with no atoms removed.
(c) $CH_2OCH_2 + 2\frac{1}{2}O_2 \rightarrow 2CO_2 + 2H_2O$

Remember **all compounds** of **C**, **H** and **O** produce **CO$_2$** and **H$_2$O** when they burn.

AQA only

# NUCLEOPHILIC SUBSTITUTION OF HALOGENOALKANES

## HALOGENOALKANES

**Halogenoalkanes** (sometimes called **haloalkanes**) are alkane molecules with one or more hydrogen atoms replaced with halogen atoms. For example:

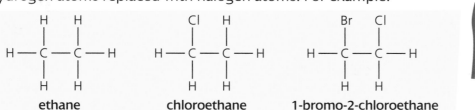

| ethane | chloroethane | 1-bromo-2-chloroethane |

> **MUST CHECK**
>
> 'Naming organic molecules', page 91

## REACTIONS OF HALOGENOALKANES

### HYDROLYSIS (REACTION WITH WATER)

> This is a **substitution reaction** – **OH** has been **substituted** for the **X** atom.

**R** = $CH_3$, $C_2H_5$ etc.

$$R\!-\!X + H_2O \xrightarrow[NaOH(aq)]{reflux} ROH + HX$$

**X** = F, Cl, Br, I

> Edexcel: **detailed** mechanism not required

---

**Mechanism for hydrolysis**

For example: $CH_3CH_2CH_2Br + H_2O \rightarrow CH_3CH_2CH_2OH + HBr$

The C–Br bond is polar. The O atom has lone pairs and a δ– charge.

> **MUST CHECK**
>
> 'Examples of polar molecules', page 27

---

**... Therefore ...**

1. The δ– oxygen atom is **attracted to the δ+ charge** on the C.
2. The **lone pair** on the O forms a **single bond** with the C: **nucleophilic attack**.

Remember: a curly arrow shows the movement of two electrons.

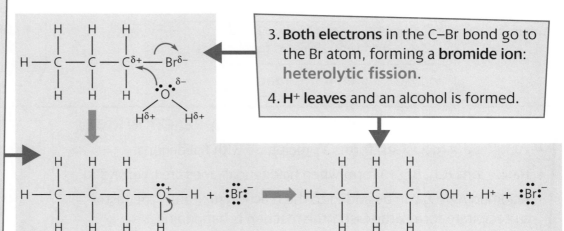

3. **Both electrons** in the C–Br bond go to the Br atom, forming a **bromide ion**: heterolytic fission.
4. **H⁺ leaves** and an alcohol is formed.

---

**Key points**

**Nucleophiles** donate a lone pair to a positively charged carbon atom. They:

- are attracted to positive charge
- are either molecules with lone pairs e.g. $H_2O$, $NH_3$ ...
- or negatively-charged ions e.g. OH⁻, CN⁻.

**Hetorolytic fission:**

- happens when a bond breaks and both electrons go to one atom, making a negatively-charged ion.

# HYDROLYSIS BY OH⁻

The hydrolysis of halogenoalkanes is **catalysed** by aqueous sodium hydroxide because . . .
. . . the OH⁻ ion from NaOH(aq) has a **full negative charge**, so is a **better nucleophile** than water.

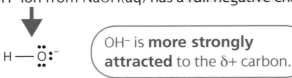

OH⁻ is **more strongly attracted** to the δ+ carbon.

Notice the mechanism for hydrolysis is the same for OH⁻ . . .

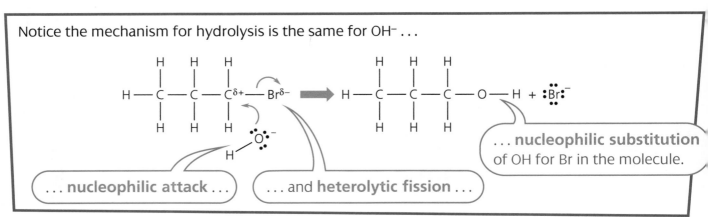

. . . **nucleophilic attack** . . .

. . . and **heterolytic fission** . . .

. . . **nucleophilic substitution** of OH for Br in the molecule.

# BOND STRENGTHS AND REACTIVITY

The **reactivity** of a halogenoalkane depends on the **strength of the C–X bond** (carbon–halogen bond).

Fluoroalkanes are very **unreactive**.

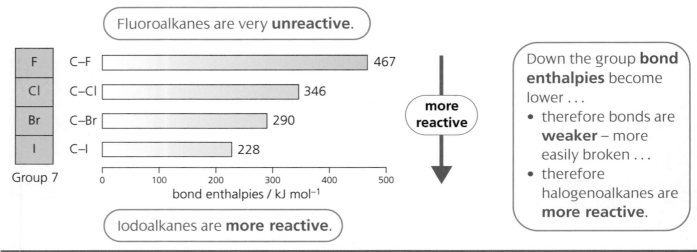

| Group 7 | | bond enthalpies / kJ mol⁻¹ |
|---|---|---|
| F | C–F | 467 |
| Cl | C–Cl | 346 |
| Br | C–Br | 290 |
| I | C–I | 228 |

**more reactive**

Down the group **bond enthalpies** become lower . . .
- therefore bonds are **weaker** – more easily broken . . .
- therefore halogenoalkanes are **more reactive**.

Iodoalkanes are **more reactive**.

## USING AQUEOUS SILVER NITRATE TO FOLLOW REACTION RATE

- Acidified **$AgNO_3$(aq)** forms a precipitate with halide ions.
- Halide ions (Cl⁻, Br⁻, I⁻) form when halogenoalkanes are hydrolysed.
- Acidified $AgNO_3$ can be added to the reaction mixture – the faster a precipitate forms, the faster the reaction is happening.

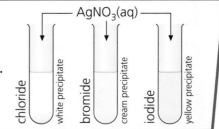

$AgNO_3$(aq)

chloride — white precipitate
bromide — cream precipitate
iodide — yellow precipitate

## WORKED EXAMPLE

1-chloropropane is refluxed with aqueous sodium hydroxide.
(a) Write a balanced ionic equation for the reaction that occurs.
(b) Draw the structure of the attacking nucleophile and identify the features of the structure that enable it to act as a nucleophile.
(c) Explain why the rate of reaction differs if the same conditions are used with 1-bromopropane.

(a) $CH_3CH_2CH_2Cl + OH^- \rightarrow CH_3CH_2CH_2OH + Cl^-$
(b)

H—O: ← negative charge
       ← lone pair

**BOTH** are important!

(c) 1-bromopropane would react faster. The C–Br bond has a **lower bond enthalpy** than the C–Cl bond and so is **more easily broken**.

# MORE REACTIONS OF HALOGENOALKANES

## NUCLEOPHILIC SUBSTITUTION REACTIONS

### REACTION WITH AMMONIA (NH₃)

Ammonia is dissolved in ethanol – **ethanolic ammonia**.

For example: $CH_3CH_2CH_2Br + NH_3 \rightarrow CH_3CH_2CH_2NH_2 + HBr$

The mechanism is the same as **hydrolysis** – see page 117.

Notice:

- Ammonia is a molecule with a lone pair – it acts as a nucleophile.
- The C–Br bond breaks by heterolytic fission.
- This is another example of a **nucleophilic substitution** reaction.

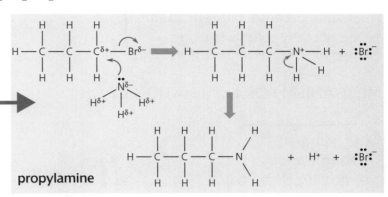

propylamine

### REACTION WITH CYANIDE IONS (CN⁻)

For example:

$CH_3CH_2CH_2Br + CN^- \rightarrow CH_3CH_2CH_2CN + Br^-$

This is an important reaction because **another C atom** has been **added** to the **chain** of C atoms – chemists use this reaction to 'grow' longer chains.

Another **nucleophilic substitution** reaction

## SUMMARY OF REACTIONS OF HALOGENOALKANES

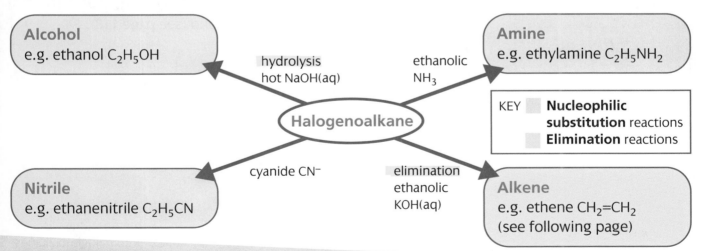

**Alcohol**
e.g. ethanol $C_2H_5OH$

hydrolysis
hot NaOH(aq)

ethanolic
$NH_3$

**Amine**
e.g. ethylamine $C_2H_5NH_2$

**Halogenoalkane**

| KEY | **Nucleophilic substitution** reactions |
| | **Elimination** reactions |

cyanide CN⁻

elimination
ethanolic
KOH(aq)

**Nitrile**
e.g. ethanenitrile $C_2H_5CN$

**Alkene**
e.g. ethene $CH_2=CH_2$
(see following page)

### WORKED EXAMPLE

These equations show how propanol can be made from propene.

Equation 1: $CH_3CH_2=CH_2 + HBr \rightarrow CH_3CH_3CH_2Br$
Equation 2: $CH_3CH_3CH_2Br + H_2O \rightarrow CH_3CH_3CH_2OH + HBr$

(a) Choose words from this list to identify the reactions in each equation:
   addition  electrophilic  nucleophilic  substitution

(b) Identify the electrophile and the nucleophile in the reactions. Explain your reasoning.

(a) Equation 1 is electrophilic addition.
   Equation 2 is nucleophilic substitution.

(b) In equation 1, HBr is an **electrophile**. It attacks the electron-dense double bond and **accepts a pair of electrons** to form a bond.
   In equation 2, $H_2O$ is a **nucleophile**. It is attracted to the δ+ C and **donates a pair of electrons** to form a bond.

# ELIMINATION REACTIONS

A hydrogen halide (e.g. HBr) is **eliminated** from the molecule ... **elimination reaction**.

## ALKENES FROM HALOGENOALKANES

**Conditions**
- **Ethanolic KOH** (note that reactants are often dissolved in ethanol because halogenoalkanes are not very soluble in water).

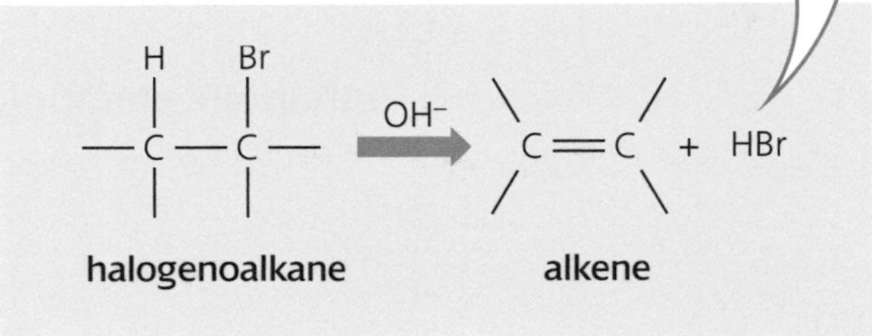

halogenoalkane                alkene

## MECHANISM FOR ELIMINATION BY OH⁻

OH⁻ acts as a **strong base** by **removing H⁺** from the molecule.

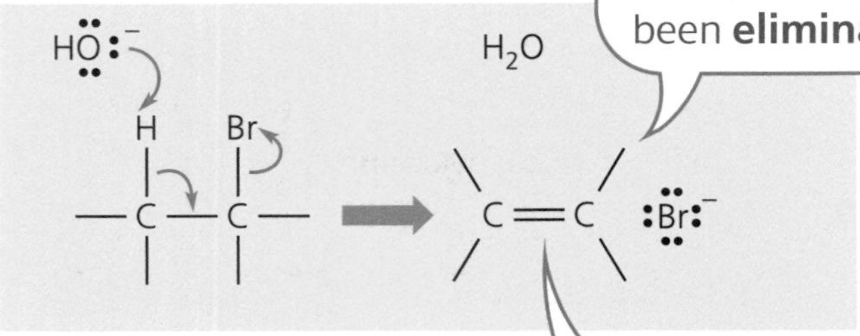

Two atoms have been **eliminated**.

$H_2O$

A **new double bond** is formed.

## BASE OR NUCLEOPHILE?

$OH^-(aq)$

... acts as a **base**:
- in **elimination** reactions of halogenoalkanes to form alkenes
- by accepting a proton.

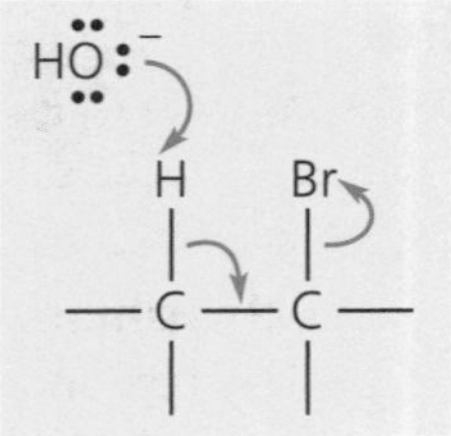

In practice, OH⁻ usually does **both at the same time**, leading to a mixture of products!

... acts as a **nucleophile**:
- in **nucleophilic substitution** of halogenoalkanes to form alcohols (hydrolysis) ...
- by donating a lone pair to form a bond (see page 118).

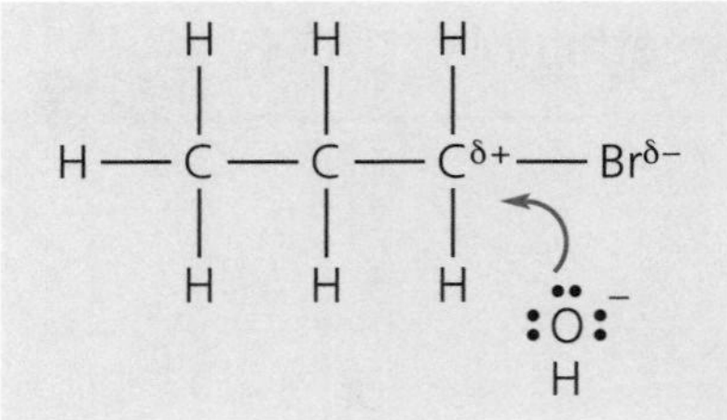

### WORKED EXAMPLE

1-iodobutane ($CH_3CH_2CH_2CH_2I$) reacts with ethanolic potassium hydroxide to form a mixture of products.

(a) Write the structural formulae for the two main products.
(b) Identify the type of reaction that forms each product.

Remember that OH⁻ reacts with halogenoalkanes by **elimination** (to make **alkenes**) and by **nucleophilic substitution** (to make **alcohols**).

(a) $CH_3CH_2CH=CH_2$
     $CH_3CH_2CH_2CH_2OH$

(b) Propene is made by an **elimination** reaction. Propanol is made by a **hydrolysis** reaction, involving **nucleophilic substitution**.

# USING HALOGENOALKANES AND CFCs

start
OCR only

## HALOGENOALKANES

**Halogenoalkanes are used . . .**

. . . for making **monomers** for **polymerisation**.

**For example**

- Chloroethene $CH_2=CHCl$ is used to make poly(chloroethene), often called 'PVC' – used for wellies.

- Tetrafluoroethene $CF_2=CF_2$ is used to make poly(tetrafluoroethene), often called 'Teflon' – used for non-stick coating on pans and clothes.

**MUST CHECK**

Page 113 for more information on polymers.

. . . for making **reaction intermediates**.

- Halogenoalkanes are important intermediates in the **synthesis** of organic compounds because they are **much more reactive** than alkanes.
- They are used in the manufacture of medicines, cosmetics, dyes, polymers, materials, etc.

. . . in place of **CFCs** and **fluoroalkanes**.

- See next page.

## CFCs

**CFCs** are **chlorofluorocarbons**. They have a very wide range of uses because:

- They are very **unreactive**, **non-flammable** and **non-toxic**, so are safe for people to use. They can be used near food and in metal machinery or containers because they **do not cause corrosion**.
- They have boiling points near room temperature so they **vaporise easily**.

**Refrigerants**

- Fridges and air conditioning systems work when a liquid coolant evaporates, taking in energy.

**CFCs**

CFC11, CFC113, CFC12

**Propellants**

- Propellants force the contents out of aerosols by evaporating when the pressure is released.

**Blowing agents**

- Expanded polystyrene is made by 'blowing' hot beads of polystyrene so that they inflate.

**Solvents**

- Solvents for cleaning circuit boards and dry-cleaning need to evaporate easily to leave the items dry.

- CFCs are suitable for all these uses because they have **low boiling points** and so **evaporate easily** at room temperature. Also, they cause no problems during use due to their **unreactivity**.

# CFCs AND THE OZONE LAYER

**CFCs** are responsible for the depletion of ozone in the stratosphere.

- They are very unreactive.
- This is due to the very high bond enthalpy of the C–F bond.
- Therefore CFCs do not break down in the lower atmosphere but travel up to the stratosphere.
- In the stratosphere, CFCs are broken down by the intense UV light from the sun.
- This produces Cl· free radicals which **catalyse** the breakdown of ozone.
- Even if we stop using all CFCs now, the problem will continue for at least 100 years – it will take that long for existing CFCs to break down!

> The C–F bond is very strong.

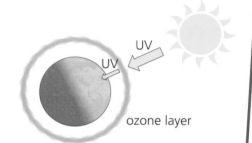

**MUST CHECK**

'Catalysts in action', page 67

## WHY WORRY?

- Ozone absorbs UV from the sun.
- Ozone depletion means more UV will hit the Earth's surface.
- This will cause skin cancers in animals.
- Many living things will die out (phytoplankton and fish in the seas are already affected) leading to food chain disruption and extinctions.

ozone layer

## HOW CAN CHEMISTS HELP?

| **1994** CFCs banned in aerosols | → Long time scale → | **2006** CFCs banned in car air conditioning |

CFCs are being phased out gradually as chemists develop replacement compounds.

### EXAMPLES OF REPLACEMENT COMPOUNDS

**Hydrofluorocarbons (HFCs)**

- This is a fluoroalkane containing H atoms.
- The C–H bond is more easily broken.
- HFCs are more reactive and break down in the lower atmosphere – the molecule never reaches the stratosphere.

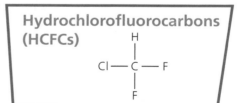

**Hydrochlorofluorocarbons (HCFCs)**

**Hydrocarbons**

$CH_3CH_2CH_3$

- Hydrocarbons are often flammable.

**Replacements are not perfect either!**
- Some replacements are **flammable** or **toxic**.
- Nobody knows for sure their effects in the **lower atmosphere**.
- They are **greenhouse gases** that contribute to **global warming**.

### WORKED EXAMPLE

The following compounds can be used as coolants in air conditioners.

$CCl_3F$   $CH_3OCH_3$   $CCl_2F_2$   $CF_3CHF_2$

(a) Which of the molecules are CFCs? Explain your reasoning.

(b) What properties of CFCs make them so useful?

(c) What are the main disadvantages of replacement compounds?

(a) $CCl_3F$ and $CCl_2F_2$ are CFCs – they contain **chlorine, fluorine** and **carbon atoms** but **no hydrogen**.

(b) They are **unreactive, non-flammable, non-toxic** and have **boiling points** close to room temperature.

(c) They are **more reactive** and may cause problems such as the **greenhouse effect** in the lower atmosphere.

OCR only

# PHYSICAL PROPERTIES OF ALCOHOLS

> The **OH group** is called the **hydroxyl group**.

## PHYSICAL PROPERTIES

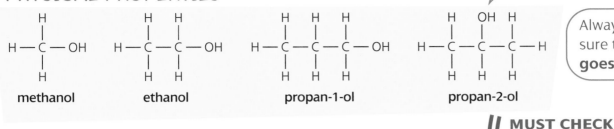

methanol     ethanol     propan-1-ol     propan-2-ol

> Always make sure the **bond goes to the O**.

## HYDROGEN BONDING IN ALCOHOLS

> The OH group forms **hydrogen bonds** because . . .

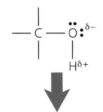

> . . . the O–H bond is **polar**, the **O** atom has a δ– **charge** . . .

> . . . and the **shape is bent** due to the lone pairs on the O atom.

> **MUST CHECK**
> Pages 31 and 25 for more about hydrogen bonding and shapes of molecules.

### Therefore

**Alcohols have much higher boiling points than alkanes** because:

- Alkanes have **van der Waals forces** between molecules.
- Alcohols have **hydrogen bonding** as well as van der Waals forces between molecules.
- The forces between molecules must be broken when the liquid boils.
- Hydrogen bonding is the strongest intermolecular force.
- Therefore more energy is needed to break the hydrogen bonds.
- Therefore the boiling points of alcohols are higher.

> Remember: bonds **inside** molecules **DO NOT BREAK** when they boil!

**Alcohols are soluble in water** because:

- Hydrogen bonds can form between alcohol molecules and water.
- This is a very important property because ethanol can be used as a solvent for reactions between organic and ionic compounds that do not normally mix – e.g. KOH and halogenoalkanes, see page 119.

## BOILING POINTS OF ALKANES AND ALCOHOLS

| Alkane | Boiling point / °C | Alcohol | Boiling point / °C |
|--------|--------------------|---------|--------------------|
| $CH_4$ | −164 | $CH_3OH$ | 65 |
| $C_2H_6$ | −89 | $C_2H_5OH$ | 79 |
| $C_3H_8$ | −42 | $C_3H_7OH$ | 97 |
| $C_4H_{10}$ | −1 | $C_4H_9OH$ | 117 |

> Boiling points increase down the series because the strength of van der Waals forces increase as the molecules get bigger.

> Alcohols have higher boiling points due to hydrogen bonding.

> Notice that the alcohols are a **homologous series** because **each differs from the last by $CH_2$**.
> General formula: $C_nH_{(2n+1)}OH$

# INFRARED SPECTRA

start
OCR only

## USING IR SPECTRA TO IDENTIFY MOLECULES

**Infrared spectra** are different for different molecules.

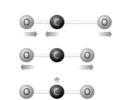

- Bonds absorb infrared (IR) radiation – this makes the **bonds vibrate**.
- Different bonds absorb IR of **different wavelengths** (wavenumbers).

Therefore the IR spectrum of a compound can be used to identify it.

- **Most molecules** contain C–H.
- **Alcohols:** look for C–O and O–H peaks.
- **Carboxylic acids** have C=O AND O–H.

| Bond | Compound | Wavenumber / cm$^{-1}$ | Intensity |
|------|----------|------------------------|-----------|
| C–H | alkanes | 2850–2950 | m–s |
| O–H | alcohols | 3580–3670 | s |
| O–H | hydrogen-bonded alcohols | 3230–3550 | s (broad) |
| O–H | carboxylic acids | 2500–3300 | m |
| C–O | alcohols and carboxylic acids | 1000–1300 | s |
| C=O | carbonyl compounds e.g. aldehydes, ketones and carboxylic acids | 1680–1750 | s |

m = medium   s = strong

## LOOKING AT SPECTRA

**Hint: look for specific peaks** (OH and C=O); **ignore the others!**

**Propanone**

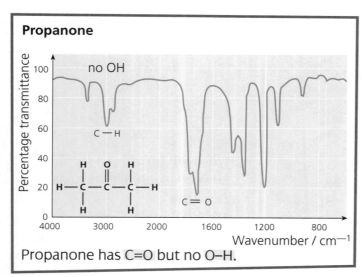

Propanone has C=O but no O–H.

**Ethanoic acid**

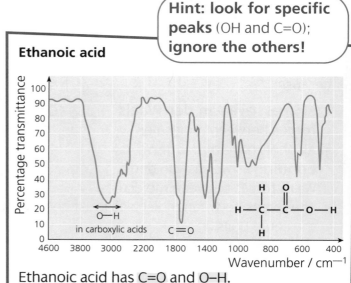

Ethanoic acid has C=O and O–H.

## WORKED EXAMPLE

This is the IR spectrum for an organic compound
(a) Which bonds cause peaks A and B?
(b) Which of the following compounds would give this IR spectrum?

propanoic acid

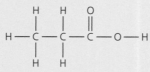

butanone

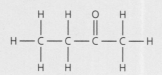

butan-1-ol

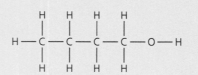

(a) A is O–H; B is C–O.
(b) Butan-1-ol because it contains both C–O and O–H bonds. There is no C=O peak on the spectrum.

end
OCR only

# ALCOHOLS IN INDUSTRY

start
OCR and AQA only

## USES OF ALCOHOLS

### ETHANOL

**Alcoholic drinks**

- **Fermentation** produces **alcoholic drinks** that contain ethanol – e.g. wine and beer.
- **Distillation** of fermented liquor makes more concentrated **spirits** – e.g. brandy and whisky.

**Ethanol $C_2H_5OH$**

**Solvent**

Ethanol is:

- used as a solvent in **medicines**, **cosmetics** and **perfumes** as it is **non-toxic** in small quantities
- used in **industry** as a solvent for **detergents**, **inks** and **coatings**
- mixed with **methanol** and sold as '**methylated spirits**' as a household solvent.

**Fuel**

Ethanol is used as a **fuel for cars**:

- in countries with **limited oil reserves** – e.g. Brazil
- as a **renewable** alternative to petrol.

### METHANOL

**Petrol additive**

Methanol improves the **efficiency of combustion** of petrol.

**Methanol $CH_3OH$**

**Feedstock**

Methanol is an important **feedstock** in the production of:

- **polymers** and **plastics** such as Terylene and Perspex
- other compounds to be used as **petrol additives**.

**MUST CHECK**

'Better petrol', page 103, for more about fuel efficiency.

## ANNUAL PRODUCTION

Huge quantities of both alcohols are made and used.

### UK

ethanol ⬛ 330 thousand
methanol ⬛ 500 thousand

0   100   200   300   400   500
**thousand** tonnes

### WORLD

ethanol ⬛ 1.3 million
methanol ⬛ 33 million

0   10   20   30   40
**million** tonnes

# INDUSTRIAL MANUFACTURE OF ETHANOL

Ethanol is manufactured in 2 ways:

1. by **fermentation**

2. from **ethene**

## FERMENTATION

In the UK, this process is used to make alcoholic drinks. In some countries, fermentation produces ethanol for car fuel.

**Conditions**
- Yeast
- 25–45°C
- No air

> **Glucose** is made from **sugar crops** (beet or cane). Yeast uses **glucose** as **food** and produces ethanol as a waste product of respiration.

$$\underset{\text{glucose}}{C_6H_{12}O_6(aq)} \xrightarrow{\textbf{fermentation}} \underset{\text{ethanol}}{2CH_3CH_2OH(aq)} + 2CO_2(g)$$

> **Yeast** is a **living organism**:
> - It produces ethanol by **anaerobic respiration**.
> - **Air** must be kept out or the yeast respires **aerobically = no alcohol**!
> - The process must take place in a narrow temperature range or the yeast dies.

> A **dilute solution** of ethanol is made – the yeast dies when the concentration rises over about 15%.

> Carbon dioxide is the **waste product**.

## ETHANOL FROM ETHENE

Hydration of ethene is the main method of production of ethanol for industrial use.

> Ethene from **cracking alkanes** from crude oil.

**MUST CHECK**

Page 110 for more about this process.

**Conditions**
- 70 atm
- 300°C
- $H_3PO_4$ catalyst

$$\underset{\text{ethene}}{CH_2{=}CH_2(g)} + \underset{\text{steam}}{H_2O(g)} \xrightarrow[\text{acid catalyst (H}^+\text{)}]{\text{high temperature}} \underset{\text{ethanol}}{CH_3CH_2OH(l)}$$

> This is an **addition** and a **hydration** reaction – water is added.

### WORKED EXAMPLE

Alcoholic drinks are made by fermentation. Ethanol for use in industry is made by hydration of ethene. Discuss the advantages and disadvantages of each method of production.

| Fermentation | Hydration of ethene |
|---|---|
| **Advantages of fermentation** <br> • Uses **sugar**, which is **renewable**. <br> • **Drinks** made by fermentation have **varied flavours** and characters. | **Advantages of hydration** <br> • It is a **continuous process**. <br> • **Quantity and quality** can be controlled more reliably. <br> • Produces **98% pure** ethanol. |
| **Disadvantages of fermentation** <br> • Large scale growing of sugar crops is more difficult in **cooler countries**. <br> • It is a **batch process** – it is more difficult to control **quality and quantity** of the product. <br> • Produces **dilute ethanol** as an **impure mixture**. <br> • **Distillation** to produce pure ethanol for industry is **expensive** as it uses a lot of fuel. | **Disadvantages of hydration** <br> • Uses **ethene** from crude oil, which is **non-renewable**. <br> • Some countries have **no oil resources**. <br> • Pure ethanol has almost **no taste**. |

> Look at the **number of marks available** in exam questions – be sure to make enough points to gain all the marks!

*end*

OCR and AQA only

# REACTIONS OF ALCOHOLS

## PRIMARY, SECONDARY AND TERTIARY ALCOHOLS

| Type of alcohol | Primary (1°) | Secondary (2°) | Tertiary (3°) |
|---|---|---|---|
| **Explanation** | OH attached to **a C atom that joins to one other carbon** | OH attached to a **C atom that joins to two other carbons** | OH attached to **a C atom that joins to three other carbons** |
| **Example** | ethanol | propan-2-ol | 2-methylpropan-2-ol |

## OXIDATION OF ALCOHOLS

> **MUST TAKE CARE**
> - Always draw the C–O bond clearly to the O atom!

**primary alcohol** — ethanol — **oxidises to** → **aldehyde** — ethanal — **oxidises further to** → **carboxylic acid** — ethanoic acid

*Different products!*

**secondary alcohol** — propan-2-ol — **oxidises to** → **ketone** — propanone

**tertiary alcohol** → **Does not oxidise!**

> **MUST REMEMBER**
>
> | Type of compound | Functional group |
> |---|---|
> | aldehyde | $-C\overset{O}{\underset{H}{}}$ |
> | ketone | $-\overset{O}{\underset{}{C}}-$ |
> | carboxylic acid | $-C\overset{O}{\underset{OH}{}}$ |

> Compounds containing $C=O$ are **carbonyl compounds**.

### OXIDATION OF PRIMARY ALCOHOLS

**1. Conditions**
- Add **acidified** $K_2Cr_2O_7$
- Room temperature

*Different **conditions**, different **products**.*

**2. Conditions**
- Add **acidified** $K_2Cr_2O_7$
- Reflux

**[O]** represents an **O atom** from the **oxidiser**.

ethanol → ethanal (an aldehyde)
$$CH_3CH_2\textbf{OH} + \textbf{[O]} \longrightarrow CH_3C\overset{O}{\underset{H}{}} + H_2O$$

ethanol → ethanoic acid (a carboxylic acid)
$$CH_3CH_2\textbf{OH} + 2\textbf{[O]} \longrightarrow CH_3C\overset{O}{\underset{OH}{}} + H_2O$$

*More oxidation*

> **Ethanol** in wines oxidises to form **ethanoic acid** if air gets in during storage. This makes the wine taste **sour**.

## OXIDATION OF SECONDARY ALCOHOLS

**Conditions**
- Add **acidified K₂Cr₂O₇**
- Reflux

propan-2-ol

$$CH_3-\underset{\underset{\displaystyle OH}{|}}{CH}-CH_3 \;+\; [O] \;\longrightarrow\; CH_3-\underset{\overset{\displaystyle O}{\|}}{C}-CH_3 \;+\; H_2O$$

propanone (a ketone)

**2° alcohols** react at **room temperature** but are usually **refluxed** to get a **good yield**.

### MUST REMEMBER

| Primary alcohol | Secondary alcohol | Tertiary alcohol |
|---|---|---|
| aldehyde carboxylic acid | ketone | does not oxidise |

Acidified potassium dichromate(VI), K₂Cr₂O₇, acts as the **oxidiser**. During the reaction ...

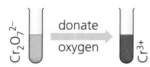

donate oxygen

$Cr_2O_7^{2-}$     $Cr^{3+}$

orange Cr₂O₇²⁻ ions ... form ... **green Cr³⁺ ions**

Test for primary and secondary alcohols: both turn acidified potassium dichromate(VI) from orange to **green**.

**Definitions of oxidation:**
- **Gain of oxygen**
- **Loss of hydrogen**
- ✔ Both definitions work for these reactions.

## DEHYDRATION OF ALCOHOLS

**Conditions (lab)**
- Use a **dehydrating agent**
- Reflux

This reaction is an example of ...
**dehydration** and **elimination**
because a **water molecule (H₂O)** has been removed.

Examples of dehydrating agents:
- **Conc. H₂SO₄(l)** (sulphuric acid)
- **Conc. H₃PO₄(l)** (phosphoric(V) acid)
- (Industrial only) **hot 'pumice'** Al₂O₃

ethanol        ethene (an alkene)

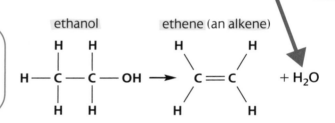

## WORKED EXAMPLE

(a) Name the product and describe what you see when acidified potassium dichromate(VI) is added to the following alcohols at room temperature.

(i) propan-1-ol, CH₃CH₂CH₂OH   (ii) propan-2-ol, $H_3C-\underset{\underset{\displaystyle H}{|}}{\overset{\overset{\displaystyle OH}{|}}{C}}-CH_3$   (iii) 2-methylpropan-2-ol, $H_3C-\underset{\underset{\displaystyle CH_3}{|}}{\overset{\overset{\displaystyle OH}{|}}{C}}-CH_3$

(b) Write equations for the reactions that occur in (a).

(a)

| | Name of product | Colour change |
|---|---|---|
| (i) | propanal | orange → green |
| (ii) | propanone | orange → green |
| (iii) | no reaction | stays orange |

At **room temperature**, product is an **aldehyde**.

Both **primary** and **secondary** alcohols turn K₂Cr₂O₇ from orange to **green**.

Tertiary alcohols are **not oxidised**.

(b) (i) $CH_3CH_2CH_2OH + [O] \longrightarrow CH_3CH_2C\overset{\displaystyle O}{\underset{\displaystyle H}{\big\langle}} + H_2O$

(ii)

$$H_3C-\underset{\underset{\displaystyle H}{|}}{\overset{\overset{\displaystyle OH}{|}}{C}}-CH_3 + [O] \longrightarrow H_3C-\overset{\overset{\displaystyle O}{\|}}{C}-CH_3 + H_2O$$

# MORE REACTIONS OF ALCOHOLS

## COMBUSTION

All alcohols burn:

- Ethanol is used as a fuel in cars in some countries – ethanol fuel is fermented from sugar cane in Brazil.
- Methanol is used as a fuel in 'spirit burners' for camping and outdoor pursuits.

**MUST CHECK**
- Pages 99 and 125 for more about fuels.

**ethanol**

$$C_2H_5OH(l) + 3O_2(g) \rightarrow 2CO_2(g) + 3H_2O(l)$$

$$\Delta H = -1371 \text{ kJ mol}^{-1}$$

Alcohols are good fuels because their combustion is **very exothermic**.

**Complete combustion** products of alcohols are:
- **carbon dioxide**   • **water**

**Incomplete combustion** – limited oxygen supply – gives:
- **carbon monoxide**, CO   • soot – mainly **carbon**, C.

## SUBSTITUTION BY HYDROGEN BROMIDE

**Conditions**
- Reflux
- With conc. HBr, hydrobromic acid
- Catalyst: conc. $H_2SO_4$

ethanol       bromoethane (a halogenoalkane)

$$CH_3CH_2OH + HBr \rightleftharpoons CH_3CH_2Br + H_2O$$

**Substitution** of OH for Br

**Conc. $H_2SO_4$ acts as a catalyst**
- $H^+$ is involved in the reaction mechanism.
- $H^+$ weakens the C–O bond so it can break.
- Conc. $H_2SO_4$ absorbs the water formed to force the reaction to the right.

This reaction usually goes the **other way**! (See page 117.) The **C–O bond is very strong** in alcohols so **substitution reactions do not happen readily**.

## REACTION WITH SODIUM

**An unusual compound**! Sodium ethoxide is an **ionic organic compound**!

ethanol                    sodium ethoxide

$$CH_3CH_2OH + Na \rightarrow CH_3CH_2O^-Na^+ + \tfrac{1}{2}H_2$$

**$H^+$**
In the reaction, ethanol acts as an **acid**:

$$CH_3CH_2OH \rightarrow CH_3CH_2O^- + H^+$$

**MUST REMEMBER**
**Acids donate $H^+$** (protons).

$CH_3CH_2OH$   This is similar to the reaction of sodium with water:   $H_2O$

- The Na fizzes as $H_2$ gas is formed.
- Ethanol loses a proton ($H^+$).
- Ethanol reacts more slowly than water because the O–H bond is stronger.

# ESTERIFICATION

## GENERAL REACTION

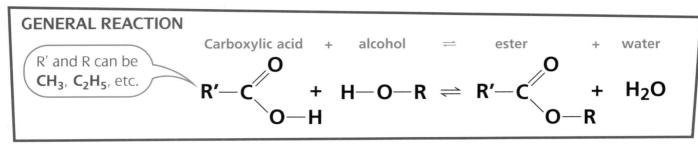

Carboxylic acid + alcohol ⇌ ester + water

R' and R can be $CH_3$, $C_2H_5$, etc.

---

**For example:** ethanoic acid + ethanol ⇌ ethyl ethanoate + water

**Conditions**
- Warm
- Acid catalyst

The **alkyl** part comes from the **alcohol**.
The **alkanoate** part comes from the **acid**.

Water is **eliminated** during esterification.

The **R' group from the acid** is joined to the **C=O**.

Must be careful to get the **ester link** the right way round!

The **R group from the alcohol** is joined to the **–O–**

$+ \ H_2O$

## EXAMPLES OF ESTERS

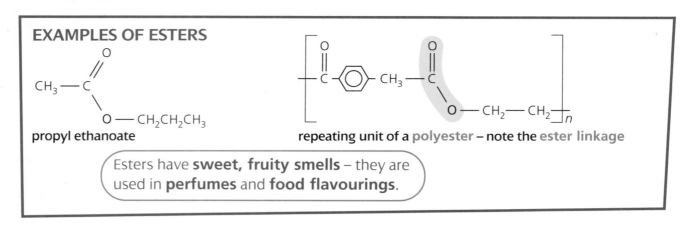

propyl ethanoate

repeating unit of a **polyester** – note the **ester linkage**

Esters have **sweet, fruity smells** – they are used in **perfumes** and **food flavourings**.

---

## WORKED EXAMPLE

Look at the following examples of reactions of alcohols.

A  $CH_3OH + 1\frac{1}{2}O_2 \rightarrow CO_2 + 2H_2O$
B  $CH_3OH + HBr \rightarrow CH_3Br + H_2O$
C  $CH_3OH + C_2H_5COOH \rightarrow C_2H_5COOCH_3 + H_2O$
D  $CH_3OH + Na \rightarrow CH_3O^-Na^+ + \frac{1}{2}H_2$
E  $C_2H_5OH \rightarrow CH_2=CH_2 + H_2O$

A  is **oxidation – combustion** reaction with oxygen.
B  is **substitution** – OH is **substituted** by Br.
C  is **esterification**.
D  is **acid–base** – methanol is donating an **$H^+$**.
E  is **elimination** – $H_2O$ is **eliminated**.

Use these words to classify the reactions:

oxidation  acid–base  esterification
substitution  elimination

end

OCR only

# INDEX

William Collins' dream of knowledge for all began with the publication of his first book in 1819. A self-educated mill worker, he not only enriched millions of lives, but also founded a flourishing publishing house. Today, staying true to this spirit, Collins books are packed with inspiration, innovation and practical expertise. They place you at the centre of a world of possibility and give you exactly what you need to explore it.

Collins. Do more.

Published by Collins
An imprint of HarperCollins*Publishers*
77–85 Fulham Palace Road
Hammersmith
London
W6 8JB

Browse the complete Collins catalogue at
**www.collinseducation.com**

© HarperCollins*Publishers* Limited 2006

10 9 8 7 6 5 4 3 2 1

ISBN-13   978 0 00 720689 6
ISBN-10   0 00 720689 5

Ann Tiernan asserts the moral right to be identified as the author of this work

**British Library Cataloguing in Publication Data**
A Catalogue record for this publication is available from the British Library

Edited by Ros Davies
Production by Katie Butler
Series design by Sally Boothroyd
Illustrated by Kathy Baxendale and Jerry Fowler
Index compiled by Indexing Specialists (UK) Ltd
Printed and bound by Printing Express, Hong Kong

You might also like to visit
www.harpercollins.co.uk
The book lover's website